MY NEWFOUNDLAND

My Newfoundland

STORIES / POEMS / SONGS

A.R. SCAMMELL

Author of
The Squid Jiggin' Ground

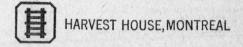 HARVEST HOUSE, MONTREAL

CREDITS

I am not a musicologist. My sincere thanks to Mrs. Elsie Anthony who helped in composing the tune to "Long May Your Big Jib Draw" and to Mr. Donald F. Cook who scored it correctly; to Mr. Huntly Cameron who scored "The Newfoundland Come Home Song" and to Mr. David Amar who scored four others of my songs. "Squarin' Up" goes to the well-known tune of "Sweet Betsy from Pike." Special thanks to my wife, Rellie, who made suggestions, most of them good, typed everything for the printer, put down the notes, in rough form, to the tunes I "made up," and made an excellent sparring partner when she differed from me over some point.

A.R. Scammell

MY NEWFOUNDLAND

Copyright © Canada 1966 by A.R. Scammell.
All rights reserved.
Library of Congress Catalog Card No. 66-23305.
For information address Harvest House Ltd.,
1364 Greene Ave., Montreal 6, Quebec, Canada.

First Harvest House edition — June 1966.
Printed by Court House Printing Reg'd, Montreal.

TO MY MOTHER
AND BROTHER CECIL

CANADIANA

PIERRE JEROME (Jean-Paul Desbiens)
THE IMPERTINENCES OF BROTHER ANONYMOUS

JEAN-PAUL DESBIENS
FOR PITY'S SAKE:
   THE RETURN OF BROTHER ANONYMOUS

PIERRE LAPORTE
THE TRUE FACE OF DUPLESSIS

PAUL SAURIOL
THE NATIONALIZATION OF ELECTRIC POWER

HUGH BINGHAM MYERS
THE QUEBEC REVOLUTION

CLAUDE JASMIN
ETHEL AND THE TERRORIST (Fiction)

HENRY DAVID THOREAU
A YANKEE IN CANADA

D.M. LEBOURDAIS
STEFANSSON: AMBASSADOR OF THE NORTH

J.F.C. WRIGHT
THE LOUISE LUCAS STORY: THIS TIME TOMORROW
(Saskatchewan)

BENJAMIN G. SACK
HISTORY OF THE JEWS IN CANADA

A.F. LAIDLAW
THE CAMPUS AND THE COMMUNITY: THE GLOBAL
IMPACT OF THE ANTIGONISH MOVEMENT
(Nova Scotia)

DOROTHY HENDERSON
THE HEART OF NEWFOUNDLAND

A.A. SHEA
BROADCASTING: THE CANADIAN WAY

CONTENTS

Introduction

STORIES

POEMS

SONGS

INTRODUCTION

Newfoundland... the squid jigging ground... Arthur Scammell. One word leads to the other, for he is our native bard and we are proud of him — long may his big jib draw!

Arthur Scammell came from rocky, near-treeless Change Islands in Notre Dame Bay. My family came from neighbouring Exploits Island. Our people fished for cod, lobsters and herring; they grew potatoes and cabbages, built their own houses and their own schooners which they sailed, log-loaded with salt cod, to Europe through the autumn gales. At home they went regularly to church to praise God for their good fortune. They bore names from the West country and spoke with a Dorset or Devon lilt in words you hear now only in a pub on the fringe of Exmoor Forest or in the one on Clovelly beach — unless, like Scammell, you recall them from your childhood and use them for the sheer visceral delight of it.

In Scammell's childhood and mine, we learned to handle a dory soon after we learned to walk, jigged our first tomcod when our arms could scarcely bear the weight of tarred line, and we sat on warm beachrocks to suck the goodness from lobster bodies we cadged from our grandpas' canning sheds. We were not aware of being deprived; we were happy.

From this background came Arthur Scammell, poet and teacher. Before he left home to try his luck in Canada, he taught school in Bonne Bay where he lived, as I do now, with majestic hills shadowing deep bays and where he met his wife whose family are now my friends and neighbours. Here he wrote "Gros Morne — Bonne Bay", as true a piece of verse as you can find, of the lovely smooth mountain which broods over our landscape and fills our eyes with beauty — which Scammell still remembers, after thirty years a schoolmaster in Montreal.

His memory has weeded out the ugly and painful and cultivated the lovable in his people. One *could* say that his compassion overrides his critical judgment, that he sees us all through a rosy mist, (for not all Newfoundlanders are simple and honest and we have our share of rogues) but in this book, he is concerned not with our deplorable human condition which is so fashionable a topic today but with recalling some of the finest men salt water ever wet.

In "Hard Cash", a piece which generates more nostalgia than most natives can endure without tears, Scammell reflects the innocence of our ancestors in a colonial system where the clergyman was at the top of a pyramid, the postmaster at the bottom and in between were policeman, customs officer and merchant. Scammell's men and women held the entire lot on their shoulders, did the best they could and loved the human race.

They "made do" and were proud of their ingenuity with a pride strong enough to carry them buoyantly from season to season. When old age anchored them to the landwash, they took into their tiny, neat old houses the youngest son and his wife for company, but kept the governance of the family firmly in their gnarled hands — unless they were unlucky with the daughter-in-law which sometimes happens, as Scammell tells us in "Amelia". They wrested respect from the villagers and followed a well charted course to Heaven with a surety born of sailing the Western ocean.

Folk history is written in Scammell's songs for those who know how to read. There is "The Squid Jiggin' Ground", for example: running down Squires was a dangerous heresy in those days. In fact, squid jigging itself may soon be a memory; already it is a pastime for many fishermen since they now get frozen bait from the Government depot — a fringe benefit of Confederation. However, Squires and squid jigging are assured a place in history as long as Newfoundlanders regard this song as our quasi-national anthem.

And what native can read the "Six Horsepower Coaker" without a flood of memories of Sir William and the Fishermen's Protective Union which throve in the political atmosphere so well evoked in "My Political Career"? Surely nobody from Notre Dame Bay has forgotten the *Clyde* — the little steamer which hundreds of times felt her way around the islands in the fog, insinuating herself into tickles hardly broader than her beam! She probably carried us all on our first sea voyage. And I dare you to read "Outdoor Motor" without tears of laughter!

If you are a Newfoundlander, here is delight in half-forgotten words, in similes born of our preoccupation with the sea. If you are a stranger, it is my pleasure to introduce you to Arthur Scammell and to assure you that his work is true and honest and frequently quite beautiful.

Ella Manuel
Bonne Bay.

STORIES

Outport Heritage

One of E. J. Pratt's lesser poems tells of Old Bill, a New-foundland sea-dog, sitting on a wharf-grump tapping his pipe out against his wooden stump of a leg and whittling a boat with his pocket knife.

Two youths are walking lazily along, superior in their snobbe-ry, knocking off the heads of dandelions with careless canes. One of them notices the old sea-dog and nods towards him rather pityingly, "Must be a dull, uneventful life, that."

Twenty years before, says the poet, when the two dandelion murderers were drooling on their bibs, old Bill had lost his leg, fighting with a kicking wheel, "Somewhere along the track of Frobisher."

I like that poem because it puts the picture in proportion with true insight. Judged by that standard, hundreds of little Newfoundland communities, far removed from the rush and bustle of city life, are rich in true social and spiritual values. I have read some stories about Newfoundland outport life, written by visitors from other countries, and most of them played up the pathos of the hard, unrelenting struggle for existence. It made the reader feel as if he should do something for these poor, be-nighted people. Knowing something of the social picture both in Canada and in the United States, I can assure these writers that their well-meaning sympathy could be far better spent on their own regions.

Newfoundlanders in their little communities have built up something worthwhile, something not measured by the size of the churches or the material beauty of the homes. Those of us who are fortunate enough to be able to claim one of these little communities as our birthplace, look back with humble gratitude to what we owe them. Daily lessons in cooperation and kindliness, taught by simple folk who wouldn't know a vitamin if they met one, but who did know that "man does not live by bread alone." Studies in industry and hard work, presented by example more powerfully than by precept. A delightful sense of humour, real humour of character and situation, that bubbled in the darkest days. Like the old fellow who told me when I asked him how his legs were: "Not very good b'y. But I s'pose I shouldn't complain. I'm eighty years old and this is the same pair I started life with."

Environment and circumstance provided many thrilling and satisfying experiences, which developed in the young outport lad initiative, and a sense of responsibility, early in life. He knew how to row and handle a boat at an age when city-bred boys were still hanging on to their mothers' hands when they crossed the street. His urge for adventure and action was satisfied, not by the unreal, fantastic exploits of a "superman" or "supermouse", but by the exciting details of his daily life and the myriad skills and lore he had to master to keep his end up in the struggle of wresting a living from sea and land.

Above all, as one looks back, from an apartment house, maybe, where the tenants know one another only from the names on the letter boxes in the hall, one remembers more keenly than anything else the way in which everybody in the village shared joys and sorrows.

Bill Peters was sick and couldn't go in the woods to get fuel. The others built up his woodpile. Uncle Sam Jensen had a boy drowned gunning. His fishing mates showed their sympathy with the true delicacy of men who fight shy of any demonstration of their feelings: "We'll haul your trawls today, Uncle Sam; no need of you botherin'."

Our outports have their unsung heroes, modest people, who perform heroic deeds of rescue as they go about their daily work, but who, perhaps, don't even "make" the local papers. I know of one instance where a father and son were caught on the ice one spring. The ice was driven off shore and broken up, and they found themselves on a small pan. The pan got smaller and smaller and soon would be too small to support their combined weight. They both knew it. The father told the boy what he was going to do and in the night while his son was dozing, he quietly slipped into the icy water. Next day the boy was rescued.

Incidents and deeds like these were welded into the tradition of the village, told to wide-eyed children around crackling winter fires, sinking into their minds with the multiplication table. Selfishness could not thrive in such an atmosphere.

And we had a lot of fun. Maybe we didn't get our quota of orange juice. Perhaps our food was a bit short sometimes on calcium or phosphorus. We were so busy catching tomcods, "copying" pans of ice in the spring, doing chores, sailing boats, etc., that we didn't have time to chase all our vitamins. No doubt we'll suffer for it some day. But we learned many important lessons of life from the humble folk around us, that all the inventions and discoveries of modern civilization cannot lessen or cheapen.

A little incident comes to mind which dramatizes this point. I was fishing at the time with my father and brothers at Change Islands, a Newfoundland outport on the north-east coast. A neighbour ran in to see if we would take a man and his wife visiting from the city, down to the pier where the steamer on which they were leaving was awaiting them. We agreed at once and father and I jumped in the motorboat and took them to their destination. Just a routine neighbourly act. When we got there the man asked what the charge was and father said "Nothing." The man pulled out some bills and insisted on paying. "You outport people," he said, "have to learn to move with the times. You'll never get anywhere unless you forget this business of giving your time and effort without getting paid." My father was now getting nettled. This insensitive hangashore not only did not have the grace to accept our hospitality, he was pitting the fledgling philosophy of a pioneer industrial town against the centuries-old tradition of the Newfoundland outport, a tradition of hospitality and kindness to friend and stranger alike. "Put your money in your pocket, young man," said my father. "This place wasn't built on them ideas of yours."

Outport life of course did not always satisfy human needs. The chances of employment were few, apart from the fishery, and those striving for a career and wider horizons had to leave home. But it did clarify and define worthwhile patterns of behaviour which made outport life rewarding and valuable.

If you were born in a Newfoundland outport, be proud of it, as I am. When summer holidays come around I want to spend them in one of those little villages.

Above the deep boom of the sea you can hear the melody of human hearts — and the music is sweet.

Fish And Brewis

Skipper Joe Caines moved the small graple out of his way and sat down on the stage-head alongside his friend Uncle Jasper Cooper. Joe was munching a giant carrot he had pulled from the garden on his way down, and at the sight Uncle Jasper turned away his head and shuddered.

"Mornin' Uncle Jasp, you not out on trawls today? I'm not out 'cause I had some hayin' to do. I mowed a bit there in front of the cellar an' then me legs give out again. I figgered though that everybody else was out except me. What's the trouble? No bait?"

"Plenty of bait, Joe boy. To tell the truth I don't feel so good. Stummick's been botherin' me."

"That so? I was 'lowin' now you got Mary home from the States to cook for you, you'd have it a lot better than you have had it since your missus passed away last March."

"Cook for me!" Uncle Jasper's high cackle had a touch of hysteria in it. "That's the trouble. She don't cook for me. Mary's got a lot of new-fangled notions about grub. Says we've been eatin' wrong all our lives. She got books and everything to prove it. She says all that's wrong with you is that you don't eat brown bread."

Joe's teeth stopped half-way through the carrot. "Did she learn that when she took her nurse's trainin'?"

"I spose so." Uncle Jasper sighed. "All she talks about is vitamines, that's little things in your grub that's supposed to keep you healthy. There's millions of 'em accordin' to Mary. She only been home three weeks an' I han't had a square meal since she come. Aranges an' salads, that's what I been livin' on. Or bidin on I should say. If it don't alter soon I won't have strength enough to row out to me trawls, let alone pick the fish off." Here the old man took out his pipe with trembling hands and began to fill it from a new plug.

"Mary's even trying to make me give up baccy. Says there's nickleteen in it. Whatever that is. No, that's not a vitamine Mary says 'tis poison. But the way I got it figgered out the nickle-teen might kill the vitamines. That's me only hope."

"Look here Jasp, you're in a bad way." Joe tried to cheer him up. "Here, have the rest of this carrot. I don't like 'em much raw."

"No boy, can't touch it. I liked a raw carrot as well as the next one atween meals. But I'm turned agin 'em now, teetotally turned. To see one of the red divils grinnin' up at me from a dry dinner plate, chock full of vitamines accordin' to Mary and with no duff on the heel of it — No Joe, makes me shudder."

Joe threw the carrot top in the water and took out a battered briar. "You sure got a problem, Uncle Jasp. Why don't you take a stand and tell Mary to cook what you want to eat?"

The old man puffed at his pipe. "Well Joe, in the first place you don't know Mary. She's mighty sot on this vitamine business. And then again I thought at first there might be something in it. You know, she bein' away to the States an' a nurse. Then I hoped after a day or two she'd kinda get over it. But she's gettin' worse. I tell 'ee she's gettin' worse!" His voice rose again in desperation. "She got menus plastered all over the kitchen walls for every day in the week. Only last night she was sayin' liver was good for night-blindness. Now look, Joe, did you ever know me to be night-blind?"

"No, Jasp. can't say I have."

"Darn right you can't. I can pick me way home on a dark night from a game of cards now as well as ever I could. But just because I feel through a hole in the flake-longers one night on the way up from the fish stage, Mary thinks I'm night-blind. Now she'll have her eye on the liver of everything that's killed in this harbour from a bull-bird to the government bull. An' I never could come liver."

Joe patted his friend's arm. "Now, now skipper don't give way to it." Suddenly he had an idea. "I'll tell you what. Come up to my house to dinner. We got fish and brewis."

"Fish and brewis?" Uncle Jasper's tone was reverent. "And scruncheons?"

"And scruncheons. Mary needn't know. And if she does, what odds?"

"If I can get outside a good meal of fish and brewis once more I think I could stand up to her."

"That's the ticket Jasp. There Jane's calling. Nothing like fish and brewis to take the taste of them salads out of your mouth."

A few minutes later Jane placed a heaped-up plate before her guest. Joe beamed.

"There you are skipper. Not a vitamine in a skiff-load. And we got doughboys an' 'lasses sauce comin' up."

"By golly Joe," Uncle Jasper said an hour later, "I feel like I could haul every trawl out there with one hand tied behind me back. And I think I'll have a little talk to Mary tonight about vitamines A, B, and C. And I might touch on D and E."

Mary was down on the stage-head that evening when her father came in with half a punt-load of cod. She watched him pitch-fork the big ones up on the stage-head.

"Gee, dad you must be strong. The food I'm giving you must be agreeing with you all right in spite of your complaints. Did you eat all those raw onions I put in your bread-box?"

The old man avoided her glance. He was thinking of how he had hooked those same onions on the last five trawl-hooks when his caplin ran out.

"Yes, m'dear. I lowered 'em down out there on the trawl."

"That's good. Now come up to supper." After the lettuce and cabbage salad and fruit cup washed down with ovaltine, the old man thought he'd better make his stand before the memory of the fish and brewis wore off.

"Look here Mary, I'm gettin' tired of this kind of food. I want some herrin' and potatoes cooked, an' salt beef and doughboys an' fish and brewis. Something with ballast to it."

"Now, father, do we have to go through all that again? What's the good of my learning anything new if you won't let me put it into practice? By the way, I've been worrying about your minerals today. You haven't had much iron lately."

"Iron? Do you mean to tell me I got to eat iron?"

"Certainly dad. Without iron your blood gets too thin and watery."

"Well, that's better than gettin' gallstones. Alec Dowell used to chew on wire nails and that's what he died with — gallstones." Then sarcastically, "Howsumever, if you're set on it Mary, cook it my way will you? Let's have graplesoup. I got an old trawl-graple down stage with one claw gone, that I bet'll make a snortin' pot of soup. I won't even take off the half-a-fathom of tarred Manila rope that's on it. That'll do for seasonin'. Har! har!"

Uncle Jasper's laugh had an edge of hysteria to it. While Mary's back was turned he daringly reached up his hand, unfastened a recipe for carrot-casserole from the wall and stuck it in the flame of the stove fire for a pipe-lighter. Leaving clouds of indignant smoke behind him in the kitchen the old man went down to split and salt his day's catch.

When he returned about two hours later he said to Mary, "I brought up a fish; it's out in the porch cleaned and ready for the pot. Thought we might have fish and brewis tomorrow."

Mary hesitated. She sensed the stiffening of her father's attitude and felt some sort of a compromise was in order. She poured some hot water out into the dishpan before she answered.

"All right father. I may cook some tomorrow if you don't get out fishing."

Next day it was blowing a small gale from the nor-west in the early morning and the boats stayed tied up to the wharves. Uncle Jasp went bragging to Joe Caines about the day's menu.

"Y'know Joe, never thought she'd give in that aisy. But I spose she'll get it back on me one way or another. She was talking mineral last night an' accordin' to the price they're chargin' us this summer for sheet iron and felt tins my cost of livin' is due to rise. By the way, Joe, how are your legs today? I han't seen you out in garden this mornin'."

"No, I tried it but had to give it up. Don't seem to have any strength in 'em. I'll be glad when the hospital boat docks here.

I want to find out what the trouble is. Operator's expectin' her today if the wind drops."

"That's a good idea Joe. Dunno but I might go aboard myself for a check-up. We'll go together."

Uncle Jasper entered the house breakfast time in sparkling anticipation of the fish and brewis. In each hand he held two eggs which he had just gathered from the hen house.

"More hen fruit, Mary me maid. You'll be able to whip up another one of they snow puddins with the whites." Chuckling he went out in the porch to put them in the lard-tin where they were always kept. Before doing so however, he looked around to see how much hard bread Mary had soaking for brewis. But all he could see in preparation for the meal was the fish he had brought in the night before. Puzzled, he hurried back to the kitchen and Mary.

"Where have you got the brewis soakin' Mary?"

"We're not having the brewis this morning, father. Just the fish. We'll have the brewis some other meal. I've been telling you that you can't mix starches and proteins. There's protein in fish and starch in brewis."

"What!" The old man was horrified. "Do you mean to stand there, Mary, a born Newfoundlander and tell me you're separatin' fish and brewis? Sure, 'tis like separatin' man and wife!"

"Now, dad don't be foolish."

"Don't be foolish!" Her father was lashing himself into a rage. "I've been foolish all along lettin' you bamboozle me with your vitamines an' proteins and starches. I've been patient the good Lord knows. I've et meat without potatoes, vegetables without puddin', bread without tea, but I'm drawin' the line at fish without brewis!"

Swinging his arms and dancing with rage Uncle Jasp let go one of the eggs which promptly fell on the hot stove and fried. Mary calmly scooped it into the stove. She tried to weather the storm.

"If I'm going to cook for you father, you must eat what I prepare for you."

"But you're not goin' to cook for me any more, me fine young lady, unless you act sensible. I'll board out over with Joe Caines. An' tomorrow mornin' I'm goin' to get rid of that new wallpaper of yours," pointing to the recipe-hung walls. "I don't like the pattern. Now you get some hard bread in soak right away and I'll go out to the pork-barrel and get a piece of fatback for scruncheons. We'll have the fish and brewis for supper. It'll take that long for the bread to soak right. An' I'm not touchin' a bite till that's ready to eat, so don't spare the brewis!" He roared the last as Mary, intimidated at last by his threat of boarding out, took down the brewis-bag and went out to fill it. Her father planked half a stick of Beaver down on the table. "Nickleteen 'll keep me alive till supper time," he announced grimly.

The wind had dropped steadily during the day and around two o'clock the hospital boat arrived and tied up at the Government wharf. Many flocked aboard for medical attention of all kinds. Aunt Sally Matthews as usual was one of the first on deck. She wanted more of them pink pills the doctor had given her the spring before for her internal trouble. They had helped her a lot. Joe Ploughman, Navy Joe he was called, was anxious to get permission to take the cast off his left knee, hurt while hauling a load of birch wood for the parson. Young Billy Martin was there holding on to his mother's hand. His eyes had been sore ever since he had measles around Candlemas. The Customs officer hobbled down on the ball of one foot and the heel of the other. He had a festered toe caused by a "sparbel" in his shoe and a day's berry picking.

Uncle Jasper helped Joe Caines over the gunnel and looked about him.

"Looks like the doctor's in for a busy day, Joe. Quite a crowd here. Hello Bill, heard you were goin' to give the doctor all your teeth." His greeting was directed at a tall, lean man sitting on the cabin deck, whittlin'.

"He can have 'em all except the one I nips the castnet with," chuckled Bill. "I got two letters inked on that one so the doctor can see it. C. T. Stands for Castnet Tooth."

"He's a card, he is all right," said Joe when the laughter had died down. "Hello, looks like there's two doctors aboard this trip. Who's the doc down aft?" he asked one of the crew.

"That's Dr. Parsons. Bert, I think his first name is. Just fresh out of college I heard. He was born around these parts."

"Well I should say he was," commented Uncle Jasper. Born

and reared up right here in this little harbour and went to school with my Mary. Well, well, Bert Parsons a real doctor and back here tendin' folk he lived amongst." He muttered to himself, "Wait ill I tell Mary he's back from college. That'll take her mind off her vitamines." Then louder to Joe, "I was shareman with his father Skipper Dick, three summers on the lower Labrador. That was in the *Margaret B.*, I mind. Joe, me bucko, 'tis Doc Parsons ve got to see. He'll overhaul them legs of yours an' maybe get me straightened out on me diet. Come on!"

Dr. Parsons greeted the two cronies in his hearty way. Uncle Jasper started to brag of his close association with the young man's father.

"Ah now, me boy, them was the days. Skipper Dick, that's your father, thought the world of Jasper Cooper. Jasp, he'd say, there's always a berth for you aboard the *Margaret B*. Then turning to Joe. "Doc, this is a friend of mine, Joe Caines. You wouldn't know him. He moved down here from up the bay after you left for college. Now Joe, tell the doctor what ails you. I bet he can put his finger right on the trouble."

Joe spoke up. "It's me legs, doc. They've give right out on me lately. Been bad for some time. I can't get about at all without me stick. An' there don't seem to be any feelin' in 'em below me knees."

Dr. Parsons soon made his examination. "Well Skipper Joe, I can tell you what the trouble is. Beri-beri. It's a slow disease brought on by improper diet and lack of vitamins. Ever hear of vitamins?"

Joe looked at the doctor and then at his friend. "Better ask Uncle Jasp," he grinned. "He's the expert on vitamines."

Uncle Jasper squirmed. So there was something in it after all. Well, he didn't want to be shown up in front of Dick Parson's son.

"Well, Uncle Jasp," smiled Doctor Bert, "are you vitamin-conscious? I wouldn't have thought it."

"Not exactly doc," stammered the old fellow. "Just a few things I picked up from me daughter Mary. She's home now from the States, a nurse, and she's quite a smart girl. Pretty too. Yes, sir, a smart and pretty girl. Now I should say, if you'll pardon me doc for buttin' in, that Joe here hasn't been gettin' enough

vitamin B. I'll bet he hasn't been eatin' enough fruit or vegetable
or brown bread, an' I daresay he's been mixin' his starches an'
proteins."

"God bless my soul," Dr. Bert exclaimed. "That's just wha
he has been doing, I'll warrant!"

Now Joe came to life. "Look here Jasper, I thought you tol
me. . . ." Here he became aware that his friend was making all sort
of facial contortions at him and winking. Jasper had kicked him
twice in the shins but because of his beri-beri Joe didn't feel it
He ended lamely, "What do you mean, mixin' starches and
proteins?"

Jasper eyed the doctor slyly, watching for his reaction
"Well," he said, "like eatin' fish and brewis together in the same
mealstead of separatin 'em for different meals."

"Separatin' fish and brewis!" Joe roared in agony at the
thought. "No, no, if I got to come to that, me legs can stay like
they be. I'll be wheeled to the table in a wheel chair before I'l
do that."

"Now, now," soothed the doctor, "don't get riled up boys
There's no need of going so far as that. Separatin' fish and brewis!
Whoever heard of the like? You won't find that in any book on
diet. I think Mary went a bit too far there, Uncle Jasp, if that
idea came from her. That's more than flesh and blood could
stand. I'd like a good meal of fish and brewis right now." Then
musingly to himself, "Well, well, pretty Mary Cooper a nurse.
Why didn't I keep in touch with her?"

The doctor gave the two old codgers a little heart to heart
talk "man fashion" as Joe said afterwards, on food and diet.

"I know this is a bit hard to swallow boys," said he, "in more
ways than one, but if you don't try to see some sense in it, you'll
suffer for it like Joe there. Now, don't try to change your eating
habits all at once. You know it takes a codfish a little while to
change over from one kind of bait to another. If he's full of caplin
he won't take squid at first. Now we humans are something like
that. Ease off gradually on those heavy, starchy foods and eat
more fruit and vegetables and drink more milk and eat whole
wheat bread."

"By gum, Jasp," said Joe as they got up to leave, "looks like
we'll have to change boardin' houses. You don't like Mary's

cooking so you'll have to eat with my old woman and if I'm goin' to get well, Mary's grub ought to be just right for me."

Doctor Parsons had a twinkle in his eye as he waited to see how the old man would handle that broadside. Uncle Jasper thought of his threat to Mary and then looked at Joe stumbling to his feet and reaching for his stick. "Well," he owned up with a grin, "I guess I'll have to get used to it. I'll think of them vitamines goin' down an' tacklin' the beri-beri germs. By the way, doc, is your wife aboard?"

"Wife!" the doctor laughed. "I've been too busy getting to be a doctor to have much time for the women."

The old man struck a match and put the flame to his half-empty pipe. "Just like Mary. She was determined to be a nurse after you went away to be a doctor. That's how she come to know so much about grub. But like you said just now, she's apt to go a bit too far. That's why I wish you could have a little chat to her. You could straighten out her thinkin' about a lot of things, doc. She'd be delighted to see you again, dee-lighted. An' you could tell her — you know, what you said about easin' off on the ballast gradual-like. She'd take it better from you. Come over to supper."

"Well, now that's a thought," said Doctor Parson briskly, "perhaps I could. We're stayin' here all night and movin' on to-morrow if the weather stays civil. Yes, tell Mary I'll be there with bells on. By the way," his tone dropped confidentially, "What's on the menu, a salad?"

"No," chortled Uncle Jasper. "Fish an' brewis, doc. Fish *and* Brewis!"

Hard Cash

"He paid for it in hard cash." Such a statement could only be heard on rare occasions and about certain individuals in New-foundland outports twenty-five or thirty years ago. Nowadays, every second youngster you meet can jingle silver or peel off the odd greenback to the never-failing amazement of the old-time storekeeper. But in my boyhood days in Newfoundland it was almost impossible for a small boy to get his hands on any hard cash.

The small needs of my brothers and myself were taken care of by our parents via "the account" at the village store. We were clothed, fed and sent to school without our hardly becoming aware of any medium of exchange except the cod that father caught and that we helped to "make." Our school books too, were bought at the store — scribblers, exercise books, pencils, slates, a *Royal Reader* and a copybook. Everything went on father's account. As we got old enough to work on the "room" at ten or twelve cents an hour, "yaffling fish" we got a huge kick out of taking up the value of our earnings in those little personal necessities which meant to us gracious living. But that was later.

I remember the ritual of mother laying out our pennies for Sunday school collection on the dresser — big substantial pennies which gave a feeling of wealth out of all proportion to their face value. This penny could be lost by getting tangled in your hand-kerchief, or by being used as a bookmark to find the page of the hymn you had to learn. If this happened, and you found yourself penniless when it was time to get out your cent, there were two dire consequences. You lost face with the class when the teacher asked for your collection and marked it down in the class register book, and worst of all, your brothers or sisters might report it at home. You would then become for a day or two a family disgrace — a blood relation who didn't have sense enough to use hard cash in the way it was meant to be used.

I do not want to give the impression that we were unusually poor. We had plenty of plain food to eat and enough to wear, but actual money was scarce in almost every household. There was a bit of silver for church collection on Sundays, "small money" we called it which was a good name because those five-cent pieces were no bigger than herring scales. Sometimes we scraped together a bit of change for the odd peppermint knob and there were a few extra cents around the house Christmas time. But everything else went on the account.

It caused quite a stir, I remember, among the small-fry when we heard that a certain merchant was offering the grand sum of two cents each for horsestingers' wings. We knew them as "hosstingers" and I understand the modern name is dragonflies. Years later I found out the wings were used for cleaning the delicate insides of watches. At the time, however, we didn't enquire into the consumer angle of this new industry, nor did we bother to find out from any Government department if the hosstinger season was open or if our insect resources could stand indiscriminate and prolonged hunting of this species. Here was a chance to get some hard cash and we got it. Our social values altered. We became lower-lower, lower-middle or upper-upper in the social scale, depending upon how many of the precious wings we had collected in our "SEA-DOG" match boxes. In one week the few remaining hosstingers on Change Islands were setting new speed records, and the price had dropped to one cent. In two weeks you couldn't find one within a mile of the place, and we were considering hiring Hyde's big motor boat to go to Fogo, six miles away, for a load. Then the inevitable happened. The glutted hosstinger wing market collapsed, and I, with the rest of the hunters, was right back where I was before — just a penny above a beggar.

We used to knit trap linnet during the winter to pay for our school fees. School fees could not be put on the account and the schoolmaster wouldn't accept fish, tomcods or rounders. He turned up his nose at cod tongues and sounds, dried caplin and salted herring. He even shook his head at bake-apple jam, squash-berry jelly and "meshberries." He had to have the hard cash.

So father would bring home bales of cotton twine to be knit into trap linnet or netting for the trap fishermen. For this linnet they would pay cash — twenty cents a fathom. Don't ask me where *they* got the cash. Perhaps *they* sold hosstingers' wings too. Anyway father would say, "Now boys, every spare minute you get this winter, you've got to help me knit this twine. Get busy and fill needles." We got busy and fathom by fathom the linnet would grow in spite of galled fingers, aching backs and the black looks of three young boys whose ears were cocked to the laughing shouts of luckier youngsters playing "cat" out on the frozen cove after supper — youngsters who could find the money for school fees in some less painful fashion or whose fathers were not so education-conscious as ours.

Every day when we came home to dinner there would be so many needles of twine each, set aside in separate piles for us to knit before we went back to school. If we had something for dinner that I liked, say roasted bullbirds, or fish and potatoes with pork scruncheons, I'd ignore the needles till my stomach juices started churning. If we had, say pea soup or boiled rice (with or without figs), I'd knit a couple of needles to try and work up an appetite for it.

We used to learn Hygiene then. Not health, Hygiene. Hygiene was something you learned chapter by chapter and had very little bearing on daily habits. So father thought too, for when we pointed out to him that the book said we should rest after eating, he pointed out to us that unless we emptied our quota of needles every day, we wouldn't get the chance of learning Hygiene or anything else. So we knit the twine and went on learning by heart more and more about Hygiene. We took courage though from the last sentence on a certain page of the book containing the rules of health. The last sentence was "Are we downhearted? NO!" I don't know why the author put that in, but it certainly did me more good than all the ten or twelve health rules that preceded it.

Then came the great Christmas of our lives. I must say this for my parents. No matter how poor the voyage or how low the price of fish we always had our stockings full on Christmas morning — via the account of course. This Christmas we each got the usual toys, candies, apples, oranges, nuts etc., and then, right up in the toe of our homespun stockings a crisp, new dollar bill. Here was wealth! Here was affluence! We had evolved through the copper age, the silver age, and here we were at one smack, in the dollar era! We unravelled our stockings trying to find more, but that was all there was. I kept mine for weeks in my little money-purse (we never called them purses), and every time I was tempted to slip back into the silver age something stopped me.

Came a Sunday evening when there was a special missionary service and a special missionary collection. It had been blowing hard from the South'erd that day, and from where we lived we couldn't hear the church bell very well. So it happened that when we did hear it we had to leave for church in a hurry, and as I had been out on the bridge listening, I missed the giving-out-collection ritual. I didn't think about it until the hymn after the sermon — the collection hymn — was given out. I was just going to give mother a nudge in the ribs asking her to shell out, when I thought of my dollar bill. I had it with me, money-purse and all. It gave me a curious sense of power, detachment. Here was a financial crisis. The minister's sermon had been eloquent, the plight of the heathen heart-rending. I could help. But if I was going to spend my first and last dollar in any cause however deserving, I wanted something in return. I wanted glory. I wanted attention. How could I get this better than by putting my dollar bill in the collection plate?

I joined the singing at the second line of "From Greenland's Icy Mountains", watching for the sidesman to come down the aisle of the church. Now he was at the pew in front of us, occupied by the merchant who bought hosstingers' wings. He put in a fifty cent piece and my lip curled. The plate came to father. As head of the family he sat on the outside nearest the aisle. His voice rang half a tone louder as his quarter hit the half-dollar. My two brothers parted reluctantly with their paltry nickles.

Mother's dime followed and my moment came, just as the congregation was singing:

> *Till like a sea of glory*
> *It spreads from pole to pole.*

Casually, nonchalantly, I opened my hand and my dollar bill spread like a banner, covering all the silver from view. Father's jaw dropped. The dignified sidesman who had been singing lustily, missed half a line and nearly dropped the plate. My two brothers involuntarily started to make a grab for the greenback, then paused with open mouths from which no sound issued. Mother's alto was hopelessly disorganized. Close proximity to moneyed people always made her nervous. But from my end of the pew came high exultant notes, from one who had tasted all the sweets of philanthropy, and from whom the prospect of tomorrow's ruin could not rob the ecstasy of today.

Trap Berth

"Its a good job you've got back, my lad, your father has a rod in pickle for you!"

Sid Martin hastened towards the house at the sound of his mother's voice. True, it had been a long time since he had felt that pickled rod but you never knew, with father.

"Why mom, what's he want now?"

"Wants you to scout around the Blanchard room and see what they're up to. Your father's worried they're after that Long Point trap berth."

Sid understood the situation at once. A good trap berth generally meant the difference between a steady supply of fish when it struck, or small disheartening hauls. Every spring there was this rivalry over trap berths. His father had held the Long Point berth for years and his grandfather before that. It was the best berth in Sloops Tickle and the Martins had become fairly well-to-do from the fish it gave them, with hardly a year missing. Sid knew there was a lot of discontent among the fishermen over it. Good trap berths were scarce in that locality and why a few men should hog the best berths year after year just because their fathers had traps there, the less fortunate trapmen couldn't understand.

He had heard the remarks passed up at George Russell's store in the evenings. "Tisn't right that one or two families should have the best berths every year. No, sir, look at Big Bill Martin, his father took Long Point and Bill thinks he's got a claim on it. But the water's free to everybody."

"Why don't we make a harbour law like they did over to Burnt Cove? Over there nobody can put out any moorings or marks in the trap berths until a certain date. On that day everybody goes out and takes their berths. I know some places up on the South Coast where the trapmen draws lots for berths. That's the fairest way. But there'd be some pieces o' work if we tried to get that in Sloops Tickle."

So the talk went and young Sid couldn't help see the other men's side of it. Why couldn't his father let some less fortunate family like the Blanchards have that berth for a change? He had mentioned it to his mother once and she had been horrified at the idea. "What, let Long Point go out of the family? You must be out of your mind. Your grandfather'd turn over in his grave! Now take the small buckets and bring a few turns o' water."

Sid never got the courage to talk to his father about it. He knew it would only crosshackle him. Big Bill was very fond of his youngest boy but twelve-year-olds didn't give fathers their opinion on the serious business of making a living.

As he ran down the narrow path to the net loft where he knew the men were working, Sid wished they wouldn't send him over across the Tickle to play with Bert Blanchard before they had traps out. Not that he didn't like to play with Bert. He liked Bert a lot, they were the best of friends but he felt kind of cheap going there to spy around on what the men were doing.

He entered the loft where is father, two brothers, Jim and Andrew, and one shareman, Lige Coish, were busy putting the bottom in the trap with twine-filled needles. Big Bill spoke.

"Sid, go over to Blanchard's and keep an eye on what they're doing. Take the rodney. I had the spy-glass on their room this morning. Looks to me like they're getting ready to set a trap. You can pretend you came over to play with young Bert. Here, fill this needle for me afore you go."

Sid began filling the needle with the barked cotton twine all ready balled off.

"What do you think, dad, he might be after Long Point?"

"Don't know son. Can't take no chances. Jim Parsons was out shooting tickle-aces yesterday and he told me there was no

nark there in the berth. Ice must have carried away the killick
ınd pole I had on that codnet there.''

Lige, the shareman, cut off a wad of tobacco and carefully
towed it away inside his right cheek. "Harry Blanchard's been
ɔragging that he's going to have a trap berth this summer and a
good one. He didn't do nothin' off a trawl last year. *John Dooley's
ɔunt an' the Weewawee.*''

Sid grinned. Lige had a curious habit of beginning or ending
ı speech with a line or two of any ballad, jig, or song that
happened to pop into his head. "John Dooley's Punt" was a
favourite source of quotations.

Big Bill snorted. "Harry Blanchard's no fisherman nor his
father before him. All he's good for is to run down better men
than he is. Got the needle full Sid? Now get going.''

Sid left. Lige was just starting on:

> *A great big sea hove in Long Beach*
> *An' Granny Snooks she lost her speech.*

Bert Blanchard and his mother were sawing wood when Sid
entered the yard. After a few words of greeting he picked up the
axe by the chopping block and started splitting the spruce and fir
junks.

"Your crew busy getting traps ready these days I spose?"
queried Bert.

Sid nodded. "Ours is too," Bert said. "Finished bark boiling
last week.''

"Oh, I do hope we get some fish this summer." Mrs. Blanchard spoke wistfully. "Harry didn't do anything last year and
Mary does want to finish her course at the General Hospital. One
more turn of dry wood, Bert, for splits.''

"Won't she be able to?" asked Sid.

Mrs. Blanchard shook her head. "We won't be able to manage
it if there's no fish. It'll break Mary's heart if she can't go back
in September. She was doing so well too. Why she knows almost
as much as Dr. Parsons now.''

"I'll say she do," Bert bragged. "One of our sharemen chopped
his foot last week making a bobber, and Mary cured it up in no
time. Didn't even fester.''

After they had the wood piled in the wood-box Bert and
Sid went down to the fishing room where the men were. Sid

could see at once that they had their trap just about ready to g
in the water. Grapnels, big and small were laid out on the stag
head with moorings neatly coiled on the claws. There were tw
big heaps of linnet; one Sid knew was the trap and the othe
the leader, a straight piece of linnet about 50 fathoms long whic
would lead the fish into the trap doors. The Blanchards made n
mention of what berth they intended to take and Sid didn't as
them. He remembered Mrs. Blanchard's face when she spok
about Mary and he found himself wishing they could have h
father's berth, Long Point. But what could he do about it? H
couldn't tell them to go and take it nor could he tell them rigl
out that there was no mark there in the berth.

"I s'pose your father got his moorings out all ready?" M
Blanchard said casually, coiling two Manila door-ropes on th
splitting table.

Sid paused a moment before he said, "No, we got nothin
in the water yet. Daresay we'll be at it tomorrow though."

When he got home Sid told his father the Blanchards wer
just about ready to set. He couldn't bring himself to tell a li
about it.

"I wish they had a good berth, dad. Mrs. Blanchard wa
saying if they don't make a good voyage Mary won't be able t
finish her nursing course."

"That'll be too bad," said Big Bill. "Blanchard will have t
take his chance like the rest of us. Course if we get more fis
than we can handle at Long Point we'll give him some. Turn i
early tonight, boys. We'll be pointin' her nose for Long Point soo
as 'tis light enough to see. Got to make sure nobody forelaids us.

Sometime in the night Sid woke. He lay quiet for a fe
minutes listening to the lapping of the waves on the landwas
beneath his open window. From his bed he could see the moonligh
glistening on the water. Then he heard it, a faint pop-pop, i
the distance. There was a motorboat on the go. Who could tha
be? Was it, could it be Blanchard's? It sounded like their old si
horse-power Coaker engine. He wriggled under the bedclothe
with excitement. He wouldn't rouse his father anyway. If it wa
Blanchard it was too late to do anything about it. It was som
time before he got off to sleep again.

His father's raucous "Heave out boys!" woke him the secon

time. Dawn was just breaking and after a hurried mug-up they started getting the trap down skiff. They just had the leader aboard when they heard Lige coming along the flake humming:

> *We'll rant and we'll roar like true Newfoundlanders*
> *We'll rant and we'll roar on deck and below....*

Lige lived in a nearby house with his old mother and went shareman with them every year.

"Old woman said she thought she heard a motorboat sometime before daylight," ventured Lige, kicking the slider off the trunkhole. I 'lows Harry Blanchard is off Long Point by this time."

"What!" Big Bill roared. He looked quickly across the tickle. "By jingo, their motorboat is gone off the collar. I bet a blast he's gone for Long Point."

"What do you expect, father?" grumbled the oldest son, Jim. "I been keepin' on ever since Candlemas about getting our gear ready. We're all behind with our work this spring."

"How did I know the rats had got in the store and chewed up so much of the linnet," thundered his father, stung to the quick. "That's what hove us back. Anyway, I thought that codnet would hold the berth. So 'twould, too, if the ice hadn't cut off the moorin'!"

Lige chucked down the last buoy and yawned. "You got to be up all night now, like the careychicks, to hold a berth. Hand along the boathook, Andrew!"

> *Please Mr. Conductor don't put me offa the train...*

Bill exploded. "Good gosh sake, Lige, hold your prate and shuff her off. Heave the wheel, Andrew. Take the tiller, Sid, I've got to whip them new buoy ropes."

Sid steered the boat out of the tickle. He knew there'd be a row if their berth was gone but he knew too that such a good fisherman as his father would get fish anyway.

Sure enough, when they steamed around the point there was Blanchard's motorboat in the berth. They had the trap out. Harry Blanchard and one of the sharemen were in the punt setting one of the backs. Before the engine shut off Big Bill started yellin'

"So you've stole my trap berth have you, Harry? Why can't you find a berth of your own without bothering other people's?"

"Them's rash words, Bill," Harry answered calmly. "Just because you've always had a trap here don't give you ownership of the water. You had no gear here, not even a mark."

"I had a codnet here," roared Bill. "Maybe you cut the rope!"

"There was nothin' showin' around here, was there boys?" Blanchard appealed to his crew for confirmation and got it. "That's the truth, Bill. I know'd you wouldn't like this, but I got to make a livin' too, you know. The law'll uphold me."

Bill Martin knew this and it made him all the madder. Bluster as he might he knew he couldn't force the other to move his trap. He threw a last taunt at his rival. "All right Blanchard, you got the berth. But havin' a good berth and gettin' the fish is two different things. You won't get the fish here that I got, I'm telling you straight. You might be a good trawl and hook-and-line man, but you don't know the first thing about traps! Start her up Andrew."

Big Bill made a new trap berth. He had had a place in mind for years on a shoal just off Long Point. Nobody had ever had a trap there before and as long as he had the Long Point berth Sid's father had never bothered to try it. It gave them fish too, though not as much as the year before.

But the strange thing to Sid was that Long Point didn't play up for Blanchard. True they got a few quintals once in a while, but nothing like the boatloads, yes sometimes two or three boatloads that the Martins used to get there nearly every time they hauled. Sometimes Blanchard even had a water-haul.

Sid knew the whole family was bitterly disappointed over the small hauls of fish. Mrs. Blanchard tried to keep cheerful but the men's downcast faces when they came alongside the stage-head took the heart out of her too. Sid went over there as usual and tried to show them that he didn't hold it against them about the berth. But if they didn't get fish it would be all for nothing. Sid was just as much concerned over it as Bert.

"Dad can't get his trap set right," Bert would say. "He knows it, but he don't know what's wrong. He'll never be the fisherman your father is."

"Guess that's so," agreed Sid. "But Bert, you simply got to get fish. What about Mary, and your mother too," he added, "This worry's killin' her I can see."

Sid used to hear his father and brothers laugh knowingly every time they passed along by Long Point. Some huge joke was tickling them. Sid wondered what it was.

"What did I tell him?" Big Bill boasted one day. "I bet the fish goes through that gulch under his leader of a rush. Well, if he don't know about it I shan't tell him."

Gulch? Sid's ear pricked up. So that was the trouble! The fish, instead of being led into the trap, escaped through the gulch before they reached the doors. He knew how that could be fixed. Not for nothing had he stayed up nights doing his homework with one ear cocked to the trap talk that went on in the kitchen. He told Bert that very day about the gulch. "Tell your father to shoot a codnet across that gulch," directed Sid. "Sound with the jigger and make sure exactly where it is and how wide. It may take a fleet of nets. I can mind now something about father always taking a fleet of codnets aboard when he put out the Long Point trap."

All of a sudden the Blanchards started getting bigger hauls. When Bill Martin heard about the first one he said, "By gum, he must have found out about the gulch and stopped it. Never thought he was that fish cute. Well, if he's man enough to outwit a codfish, my blessin' to him."

Sid went out with the Blanchards one evening. Bert wanted him to go. Mary was going too and so Sid jumped aboard. Besides he wanted to see a big haul again. He had seen his father have big hauls before but every time it was just as exciting as the last. He wasn't disappointed.

As soon as they had raised the doors the meshed fish around the mouth and V's gave promise of a good tuck. There was a smart tide running and as soon as they cut the first linnet Mr. Blanchard sent the punt out on the back to raise the wind'ard back corner. "Fish'll go out otherwise," he explained to the boys. "Put up a signal there, men. We're goin' to need help to save all the fish that's in this trap."

One of the crew tied an oilskin jacket on a pole and stuck it in the mast-hole. This was a sign to any boats within sight of it that there would be some fish to be given away as the crew had more than they could handle. Crews wanting the extra fish would make for the spot, help finish hauling the trap and take the surplus aboard their own boats.

"Keep up them loo'ard cuts."

"Get the oars and push that bag of fish from out under the keel!"

"Don't let it get around the blades!"

"Be sure and keep some linnet on the gunnel!"

Then the mad splashing and fuss as the fish broke to the surface driven by the ever-rising bottom linnet. Sid and Bert were wild with glee trying to help, getting in the way of the men and hooking a few big ones aboard with handgaffs. Mary too, sitting on the engine-house could hardly contain herself. Finally, it was dried up, about fifty quintals the men allowed. They got up the dipnets, bowl-shaped nets hanging from round iron rings and attached to long wooden handles, and soon a boat-load was dipped in.

"That's enough boys," sang out Harry Blanchard. "We got half a day's splittin' here. Now men share the rest." And the five boats that had answered the signal dipped in four or five quintals each.

"I s'pose your father is still sore," Bert said to Sid on the way in.

"Yes, I guess he is," Sid confessed. "Still I think he'll get over it. 'Tis not like we wasn't getting any fish."

"We wouldn't be getting much now if you hadn't told me about that gulch."

"Oh that," Sid grinned. "I figgered there was no sense in all that fish goin' to waste."

Buyer Must Be in Good Condition

I was much excited recently when I received a letter from my father telling me he was planning to get a new boat and engine for the coming fishing season. He had been waiting for a long time to make a good summer before he incurred this heavy expense. But last year we had been lucky and it looks like we'll put to sea in a new outfit this summer.

Although on hearing the news I felt a little twinge of regret at parting with life-long companions, I must confess my dominant reaction was one of satisfaction and relief. I have known many fishermen fondly attached to a boat or engine because of certain endearing qualities, real or imagined, possessed by the adored object — such qualities as exceptional performance, beauty of line, seaworthiness, etc. But by no forced stretch of the imagination could I endow our ancient craft and its means of propulsion with any of the above-named attributes. If in the dim mists of antiquity the boat *had* been new and sound and strong and the engine efficient and shining and capable of developing all of its 6½ horsepower, I have forgotten it. My twentieth century mind recalls only the endless docking for repairs, the search for elusive leaks, the frenzied enquiries for second-hand cylinders and spare parts in the height of caplin scull. . . .

Every summer when I arrived home one of my first questions was always the same, "How's the old motorboat?" The laconic reply was always the same too — "Leaks a drop." That "drop"

I soon discovered to be a masterpiece of understatement. When the engine was running, the oakum would loosen up in the old planking and we'd spend half our time pumping. The other half would be taken up repairing the pump. Most old motorboats shake a little from the vibration of a running motor and, of course, the occupants shake too while in the boat. But the strange thing about ours was that after you got out of her you'd still shake

The engine, a relic of boyhood days, was like all worn-out engines, temperamental. She was more than that, she was actually vicious. Great age seemed to have given her the right to defy every known law of combustion and heat. She oozed her contempt from every pore in her iron skin in all the three forms of matter, gaseous, liquid and solid. When she did agree to run, it was generally in a noisy, rebellious, grumbling way quite different from the joyous staccato performance of most Acadias.

Last summer we called in an expert engineer for diagnosis. Father was stubbornly convinced it was our lack of mechanical know-how that prevented her from giving her best. Our friend, long versed in the ways of intractable motors, took hold of the wooden pin in the flywheel (I had kicked the iron one loose in a fit of temper just after World War 1), and carefully sucked down some priming. He rocked the wheel. There was a loud groaning noise from the base. "What's that?" asked the expert, startled. We didn't tell him of course. No use spreading bad news. He snapped the wheel quickly to the left with a confident jerk. Nothing happened. My brother and I looked at each other and grinned. The old girl hadn't let us down. She was going to be difficult. After he had nearly dislocated his shoulder and raised two blood bladders on his right hand, the old 6½ (approximately) exploded for him. According to the instruction book she should have

(a) reversed the motion of the flywheel,
(b) continued the movement in an anti-clockwise direction.

She caught ahead for a few sickly pops, emitting deadly carbon monoxide fumes from the leaky priming cup, then caught astern in an agony of remorse for having started going the right way the first time. When she stopped abruptly, the expert was just going to grab the flywheel handle again but she would have none of him. She caught ahead in a roaring crescendo of sound, plough-ing the nose of the boat into the stage-head and tumbling the three of us who were sitting on the engine house, into the after-room. All this time there were sparks and tongues of flame flying out from around the base, trying to catch fire to the expert's clothes while he was still half-dazed from the gas fumes.

We picked ourselves up in a dead silence comparing casual-ties. There was a new dent in the battered gunnel and a corres-ponding dent in the bridge of my nose. Father still gripped between his teeth a broken pipestem. My brother hooked a cock-caplin out of one ear and a small thole-pin out of the other.

The expert crawled up out of the engine room gasping for air. Father spoke, "What d'ya think of her, old man?"

He shook his head slowly and sadly.

"Honest to God, Skipper, she scares me," he whispered.

My brother and I helped him up over the wharf-head. We patted him on the back and shook him by the hand, the left hand that didn't have any blood bladders.

Even we amateurs could understand just how he felt.

At the end of the trapping season when we had a good voyage ashore, we talked over the possibility of buying a new outfit. Father thought he might get something for the old boat and engine and asked me to make out an advertisement for him. My con-science and I finally came up with this:

FOR SALE. Boat and 6½ Acadia engine. Age unknown. Any reasonable offer accepted. Buyer must be in good condition. Pump and sculling oar given away free.

Mail Day For Amelia

It was mail day in Little Harbour. The steamer had just turned the point, whistled hoarsely a couple of times to alert the livyers and steamed carefully between the trap buoys and kegs that ringed the harbour entrance.

In her hen's yard a little 80 year-old woman, Amelia Jane White, heard the whistle as she was just throwing the last few crumbs of food to the clucking Rhode Island Reds. "No need to hurry," she thought to herself as she shushed the greedy old hens from picking at the helpless little balls of yellow chicks, "the mail won't be open for two hours yet."

Her daughter-in-law Marjorie called from her small cash store where she was serving a customer. "You don't have to go for the mail today granny; Mary or John can get it when they come out of school. It's too long a walk for you."

Amelia didn't answer but her old lips tightened. She didn't have any more conversation than was absolutely necessary with Marjorie. That was the safest way to get along with Harry's wife. Ever since her old-age pension cheques had been coming she knew that Marjorie was trying to get more and more of them. Hadn't she doubled the board money she paid Harry to thirty dollars a month when her cheques got bigger? And look at all the housework she was doing besides knitting and sewing for Marjorie's youngsters! Saucy little brats! They were getting more disrespectful every day. Only yesterday Mary had refused to go to Brent's store to get her some wool to finish the sweater she was doing on the quiet for the girl's birthday. She mightn't give it to her at all now. Gert, her own daughter married in Corner Brook had a girl, Pearl, about the same age and she'd be thankful with it for sure. Bill, Gert's husband hadn't had a steady job for months. Amelia wondered how they were paying the rent.

She sat quietly in her rocking chair, smoothing and picking at her starched white apron with her withered old hands. Hard, rough old hands, can't you rest quiet for a few minutes? They'd never be soft and smooth like Marjorie's. They had grasped too many rough surfaces, been soaked in too much brine in her fish-making days, helped to born too many babies, washed for and nursed too many sick folks.

The striking clock roused her. Half-past three. Time to start. It would take her old rheumatic legs an hour at least to walk to the post-office and she'd have to drop in on her sister, Phoebe Bourne. She had to get the wool too, and change her cheque. She never changed it at Marjorie's store. She wouldn't give her the satisfaction.

Marjorie watched her mother-in-law go out the gate with her walking stick and black handbag. "I knew she'd go herself when she didn't answer me just now. She don't trust anybody to get her mail when the cheques are due. I wonder what she does with all her pension money. We don't see much of it."

Harry spoke. "I bet mother knows what to do with it. She lived long enough without it, pinchin' and scrapin' to know how to put it to good use."

"Now, Harry, don't encourage her in her stinginess. Hurry up and deliver this order for Mrs. Snooks. If I didn't keep things movin' around here your mother wouldn't be able to lock her greenbacks away in mothballs in that big trunk of hers."

The first thing Amelia noticed was that Nell Waters didn't have her Monday wash out. She paused a moment by the fence and spoke to the little girl playing in the yard. "Is your mother sick today, child?" "No, ma'am." Tossing her head in disgust Amelia went on her way, grumbling to herself.

"Now sheep, cows and horses don't slow me up. I got a long way to go and not too much time. Crop the grass, that's your job, leave the road for slow old feet like mine."

A car blew its impatient horn twice behind her. Amelia didn't budge. Whenever she heard those blasted things she'd make out she was deaf as a post. She'd travelled this Little Harbour Road long before there was any of those noisy, smelly, dust-raising flamers of cars. If they came head-on they had to stop till she passed or risk knocking her down. If they came behind, they had to slow down till they reached a spot wide enough to pass her, plodding along in the middle of the road. She only accepted a lift if the weather was bad. Amelia wanted to see and hear as much as she could on her infrequent walks through the village to last her all the lonely days and nights she had to spend in the house. Sometimes the young rascals in the cars lipped her and she'd shake her stick at them.

The Blanchard women were speading out green, waterhorse fish. Amelia caught the familiar whiff of it. "Smells a bit on the slimy side to me," she thought. "They'll have to keep the rain water off that or it'll spoil." Her mind went back to when George, her husband was alive and her long days on the fish-flake. Perhaps that was what had given her such a strong old heart. Only last week Doc Smith had told her she'd live to be ninety. Not that she wanted to especially, once she got today's mail.

A steep grade slowed her. Amelia paused. Something was wrong. The road should have been level all the way. Then she saw that her feet had taken her off the main road onto the grassy tree-lined one leading to the cemetery. Oh well, she might just go in for a few minutes. "Tommy Watkins and Joe Snooks," she called to two young boys rolling wire hoops, "come and open this big iron gate for me. Wait here now for a little spell and close it when I come out."

Amelia walked over to where her husband and two sons were buried. She was panting and glad to sit down on the hard concrete frame. "Here I be again, George. Now don't fret yourself about me. I got to live out my time same as everybody. You got Jerry and Walter here to keep you company. I got Harry and the rest of them and I gets me pension money regular, thanks to Mr. Smallwood. Harry and Marjorie seems to be doin' all right with the business. I knows you was hurt when he sold all your fishin' gear and boats and used the money to start up in business. But you can blame Marge for that. Now rest easy, I'm making the last payment today."

She leaned on her stick and gave herself up to reverie. She felt right at home here where so many of her childhood friends were waiting — Becky Ferguson and Olive Hartman and Jenny Brinson and all the rest. Jenny had been sweet on George too, so sweet she couldn't be her bridesmaid. . . .

The two boys waiting with restless hoops, whistled shrilly to attract her attention. "Let's go," said Joe. "We can't wait around here for that old woman. She can close the gate herself, can't she?"

"No, I don't think she can. Besides, she asked us to do it. I'll go in and get her." Tommy touched her on the shoulder. "Come on, Mrs. White or we'll have to leave." Amelia's eyes were vacant, her face solemn and rigid. She didn't budge. "Who are you, boy? What do you want?"

Tommy was a little scared but Joe was waiting for him. He wouldn't wait much longer. "Come on, Mrs. White. I'm Tommy Watkins." His warm little hand found her thin, bony one. "We got to go now." He led her out, memories and all, between the grass-grown graves.

"Did I tell you where I was goin', Tommy Watkins? For the life of me I don't know." The two boys clanged the iron gate behind her and bolted it.

"No, Mrs. White. Was you goin' up to shop? You got your purse there."

Amelia fumbled with her handbag. The steamer blew, leaving the wharf.

"P'raps you was on your way to the post office, ma'am," offered Joe.

Comprehension came back to her with a rush. "Oh yes, now I'm come to meself. You're good boys, here's a quarter each. Now you see that loose palin'. Go and tell somebody to nail it on if you can't do it. We can't have animals tramplin' all over the graves."

Amelia picked up the mail — a letter from Gert, the *Newfoundland Churchman,* some papers and letters for Harry and the brown one, the important one. She changed her cheque at Mr. Brent's.

Her sister, Phoebe reluctantly accepted the twenty dollar bill

Amelia gave her. "I don't feel right about this, Mel. That was a long time ago my husband lent your George that two thousand dollars to buy his schooner. Why didn't you let Harry help pay it?"

"Harry don't know about it," answered Amelia. "An' if I told him, he'd tell Marjorie, an' she'd be heavin' that up to me some time when we gets into a snarl. No, this is the best way, Phoebe. Now that your Sam is gone only you and me knows about this. I wanted to live long enough to pay it off and thank God now we're all square. I can put away a bit now for me funeral."

Gert's letter dropped out of her bag. "I must take a few minutes to read that. 'Tis a good thing I went to them night school classes a few years back an' learned to read and write. Thank goodness Gert writes nice an' big ."

Phoebe left her and went to make a cup of tea. When she came back Amelia was putting the letter away. "What's the news with Gert?" Phoebe asked.

"Not very good. Bill hasn't found a job yet and Pearl just come down with pneumonia. After I haves me tea I think I'll write a letter and mail it while I'm down here near the office."

She didn't tell Phoebe how Gert's letter ended. "I don't like to ask you this, mother, but if you can spare a few dollars a month from your cheque until Bill finds a job we might be able to keep our apartment. I can't go out to work now with Pearl sick."

Amelia grasped her stick and started back to the post office to get Gert's money order. Her funeral expenses would have to wait.

Night School

Uncle Neddie leaned back in his flour-barrel chair, lit his pipe and expatiated on his favourite subject: Heducaton is like good hearty grub. Some people it hurts, some thrives on it. It all depends on their constitootion.

Last winter, for instance, we had a night schoolteacher come around to teach folks what was a little behind on their larnin'. Trim little craft she was too. Lines on her like a Nova Scotia banker. A few days after she come ashore in the mailboat, I was talkin' to Tom Dowell an' Henry Parker.

"Well, Neddie," ses Tom, winkin' at Henry, "I s'pose you'll be trottin' off to night school the winter."

"Yes," I said, surprisin' 'em. "I don't know but I will. I knocked off school at the 'Loss of the Royal Jarge', in the number four Reader. There's lots of things I'd like to brush up on." Hearin' that kind of took the wind out of their sails.

"You ought to come along too, b'yes," ses I. "After all, you haven't got much to do this winter, clear of knittin' some twine an' gettin' a bit o' wood."

That started 'em thinkin', and the result was that when school opened the first night, there was Tom and Henry with a brand-new scribbler apiece, all washed up an' combed to beat the band. Pretty Miss Nicholls, the teacher, had 'em right under her thumb from the start.

"Mr. Dowell," ses she, when school closed the first night, "will you take the fire for the first week?"

Callin' him mister an' smilin' at him like that made Tom grin all over. No wonder it might, poor chap. Tom's wife had a different name for him an' she never axed him to do something. She told him.

"Sartinly, miss," Tom answers, "I'll have that old bogey sweatin' blood."

She had plenty of patience an' determination, an' if ever a girl earned her money that one did. It took her the best part of a week to teach Henry that he'd larn to write faster if he didn't hold his pencil like a splittin' knife. When it came to 'rithmetic an' dismals (decimals she called 'em), Henry was better, but Tom was hopeless. He'd make great big ones and scatter 'em about among the figgers anywhere at all. Try as she might she never got him to call 'em by their right names. He started in by callin' 'em cast-net balls, an' nothing would change him.

I went over to Tom's one night afterwards for a game of checkers. His missus met me at the door.

"Where's the skipper?" ses I, free and aisy-like.

"Doin' his 'omework," she ses. I could see right off she was in a bad mood. "He's been at it now for two hours an' he got me nigh foolish. Keeps on suckin' his pencil an' mutterin'. Go in and talk to him."

Tom was nearly in the horrors when I went in the kitchen. He was ravin' about prices an' merchants, tellin' 'em where they could go, and givin' 'em the exact directions for gettin' there.

"What's the matter?" I asked him when I got a chance.

"Look here," he ses, "you know them sums we had to do. A can of bakin' powder and three pound of onions cost $65.00. Here's where I worked it out." He showed me a piece of brown wrappin' paper covered with what he called figgers.

"It's them cast-net balls again, Tom," I ses. "I bet you got 'em in the wrong place. Just like I thought. Now give that dismal another berth over under the lee of that six, and anchor 'en fore and aft so he'll bide thar."

When his wife come in later she was in a better mood until Tom mentioned he had to get his kindlin' for next night's school. Then she broke out again.

"Them turns of dry wood is gettin' a cuttin'," she ses. "It's about time somebody else took the fire."

I mentioned to Tom to let her bide and we sot down to checkers while his wife rocked away, knittin'. Every ten minutes she'd look up from the muffler she was doin' for him and make nasty remarks, like suggestin' that he go easy on the butter when he used it to get the balsam gum off his hands before goin' to school, and askin', sarcastic, if he had a clean pocket-handkercher, and whether Miss Nicholls looked to see if he washed behind his ears. Tom didn't say nothin' but the fierce look in his eyes made me give him two games before I thought 'twas safe to try for a king.

Henry's wife wasn't very enthusiastic about night school either. Specially after she woke up one night an' caught him talkin' about the teacher in his sleep, and wishin' he was twenty years younger. She wrote a note to Miss Nicholls the next mornin' tellin' her not to keep Henry after school, as he had to be in bed early on account of his rheumatiz.

Everything was goin' along in school number one. Tom and Henry was workin' their heads off tryin' to build up pints for prizes that Miss Nicholls told us would be given at the night school closin'.

Then something happened which made Tom and Henry forgit their rivalry for a while. The Ranger (that's our pleeceman) started to court Miss Nicholls. It was beginnin' to look serious. Tom and Henry didn't like it a bit. One night Tom missed school on account of a cold he got gettin' his feet wet breakin' the path through the snow for the teacher the night before. Henry didn't go either when he heard Tom wouldn't be there. 'Twouldn't be fair he said. If he had more pints than Tom when school closed, Tom'd be throwin' that up to him. I went over to see Tom after school was out. Henry was there rubbin' Tom's chest with goose grease. Tom's wife was just leaving. "The night-school teacher give 'im the cold," she said, "and she can cure 'im."

"Look here, Neddy," says Tom, "me an' Henry don't like this Ranger courtin' Miss Nicholls. She's too good for him, eh Henry?"

"She sure is," Henry agreed. "I got no use for that dolled-up

hangashore. He's a city man an' he thinks he can boss everybody
around here."

"I don't like him much more'n you two," I told 'em, "but
I'm afraid the teacher do. She hurried the work through tonight
because he was outside waitin' for her."

"There you are," ses Henry, disgusted, "just because this
human mistake in a uniform rolls his eyes at her our heducation
is goin' to suffer."

Tom stuck up for Miss Nicholls. "You can't blame her. I
guess she's kinda lonely an' the Ranger seems to be able to get
any girl he wants."

"Some of our own boys should be in there givin' him a run
for his money," Henry said. "When I was a young feller if a girl
like that come in the place, he'd be a smart outsider that 'ud get
'er."

"They've been tryin'," I answered, "but I guess they got
discouraged, specially when the Ranger got to winnard of 'em."

"What they wants is a little pushin'," suggested Tom. "I'm
goin' to get after Jim Humphreys. Jim ought to be able to cut
that Ranger out."

"I'll have a talk to Walter Murphy," offered Henry. "Walter's
a good steady chap. Between the two of 'em they ought to make
things interestin'."

Competition in the courtin' of Miss Nicholls picked up quite
a bit after that. Tom and Henry done a good job on Jim and
Walter. In a way, I sort of pitied the Ranger. Every night after
school Jim and Walter'd be there waitin' to see her home. The
Ranger turned up the first night, but the boys took his long
leather boots off and hinted to him that Miss Nicholls wouldn't
like being 'scorted home by a man in his stocking feet. The
teacher missed him and didn't take very kindly to Jim's and
Walter's attentions. But the Ranger was game. The next night
he was prepared for 'em. When they tried to interfere with him
he blacked Jim's right eye and broke Walter's jaw. Jim wore a
piece of out-of-season moose meat on his eye for a week. That
was the only way he could get back at the Ranger.

But now Henry and Tom had to think up another plan.
Miss Nicholls gave us all a composition to write just after that.
We could choose any subject to write on and the both of them

wrote on "Why I don't like Rangers." They had two weeks to write it in and, of course, they wanted me to help 'em, lookin' up the words in the dictionary and spellin' 'em out. I was never much of a hand at writin' and before them compositions was done I was sorry I ever agreed to be mixed up in it. Henry got some ideas during the day on why he didn't like Rangers and when he'd tell us about it at night Tom'd argue that he'd thought about the same thing and wanted it for his composition. They'd start rowin' then and I'd have to step in and get 'em to share up the pints they wanted to get down. I never saw men work so hard as Tom and Henry did over them essays. When they'd get excited over something they was puttin' down they'd press so hard their pen-nibs'd just cut through the paper or crumple up like a piece of rabbit wire. Night after night I coaxed 'em to give it up and try some easier plan, but they wouldn't hear of it. The writin' fever was in their blood and they couldn't stop.

The second week the both of 'em, Tom and Henry, got caught by the Ranger with a brace of partridge apiece in closed season. They had to pay a fine. After that I didn't go over to help 'em with their compositions. The words they'd have wanted me to spell wouldn't have been in the dictionary anyway.

The night we had to pass in our compositions Henry wasn't at school. I saw Tom pass in his and asked him where Henry was.

Tom shook his head.

"Henry," he said, sorrowfully, "is not hisself nor won't be for a day or so. When he went to look for his composition tonight before comin' to school he couldn't find it. Hunted high and low he did. He asked his wife about it and found she cleaned the lamp chimney with it by mistake and then hove it in the stove. She was goin' to get the Ranger to him he carried on so, but I persuaded her not to. That's what made me late."

Next school night Miss Nicholls kept me and Tom behind after the others left. She came over to where we was sittin' and looked at us with her appealin' blue eyes.

"Mr. Dowell," she said, low and soft-like, "you and I have always been good friends, haven't we?"

"Sure we 'ave," agreed Tom.

"I'm glad to hear you say so," Miss Nicholls continued, "but that composition you did for me hurt me, oh, so much." She put

'er 'and to 'er 'art. You know Ranger Thompson is another good
friend of mine and I want my friends to like one another. I'm
sure if you really knew him you'd like him, too, Mr. Dowell. He's
so gentle and kind."

Tom was beginnin' to squirm in his seat. "I don't like Rangers anyway, Miss," he muttered. He was sort of ashamed to bring
up about the little trouble he'd had with the law.

"But why, Mr. Dowell?" She was standin' right beside Tom
now with her 'and on 'is shoulder. "The reasons you gave in your
composition were not reasons at all. They were only prejudices.
We must be fair, you know, in our judgment of others. A Ranger
has his job to do and he must do it without fear or favour." She
turned to me. "Mr. Baker here, I'm sure as an educated man
agrees with me, don't you Mr. Baker?"

Well, she had me, round as a hoop. I wanted to help Tom
but how could I? I could see she really was in love with Thompson
and you can't argue with a woman in love. Besides, what she was
sayin' was sensible, when you come to think it over.

"I think Miss Nicholls is right, Tom," I stammered helpless.

"I knew you two would see it my way," she smiled at us, her
eyes shinin'. She was pattin' Tom's hand now in 'er gladness an'
I knew that was convertin' him twice as much as what she was
sayin'.

"Now, I'm going to tell you a secret for bein' such good
boys." She had 'er hands clasped now an' her eyes was like the
stars outside. "The Ranger and I are engaged. Isn't it wonderful?"

Tom and I muttered congratulations an' stumbled out. We
didn't say nothin' until we reached my house. Then Tom spoke.

"They'll make a fine couple," he choked. "Ranger Thompson's all right."

Them blue eyes an' the rest of it had done their work. I
didn't blame 'im. But I wondered what Henry was goin' to say.

Henry said plenty an' he said it often. He couldn't understand
Tom's change-over. You couldn't expect 'im to, of course. He
hadn't been kept in after school like me and Tom. We done what
we could with him, to get him to like the Ranger, but 'twasn't
much use. Tom even tried pattin' his 'and like Miss Nicholls, but
it only led to a lot o' bad language from Henry.

The last month of night school they was competin' agin' one

another something fierce, tryin' to win prizes at the closin'. Their nerves was all shot to pieces, stayin' up studyin', an' every time they'd meet, they'd row reglar. At last school was over and they both got one prize each for good conduct. Miss Nicholls left.

"Hello Tom," ses Zeke Brake, one Saturday night as Tom entered his shop. "You're lookin' a bit white around the gills. Night school took it out of you, eh?"

"You can't get an heducation without workin' for it," answers Tom, in a tired voice.

A Shot To Remember

Nobody need ever waste time explaining atomic energy to me. Years ahead of the scientists, I discovered it back in Newfoundland when I fired my first muzzle-loading shotgun.

I was 14, big for my age and just beginning to experience the thrill of shooting. Listening to tales of hunting birds and seals, from the lips of local gunners, I felt I was old enough to hunt what they hunted and shoot the same type of guns. Only dad didn't think so. Neither did mother.

I was tired of just being allowed to use a No. 12 breech-loading cartridge gun. Dad and the rest of the gunners around used muzzleloaders most of the time. Because of the heavy load you could cram into them and their ability to scatter shot, they could do greater execution among a flock of birds than the more modern breechloader. This was an important consideration when you had to get the greatest amount of food with the least expenditure of ammunition.

There was a point of land near our house along which sea-birds flew in the early dawn. It was the custom to hunt them either in small row-boats, or from blinds built at strategic points on the shore. They were very edible and provided a much needed change of diet, especially in the spring when larders were low.

My brother Cecil and I had been getting up early for a good many mornings and going over on the point, but the wary canvasbacks wouldn't fly near enough.

"Ah! what we need is a muzzleloader!" we had complained bitterly to each other morning after morning, as we watched flocks of ducks fly past, too far for our despised No. 12 to do more than make them swerve or knock out an occasional brown feather.

One morning when dad was away we decided to try our luck with a muzzleloader. The two of us rose from our beds, stealthily reaching for our clothes in the cold dark of the bedroom. We crept downstairs noiselessly, mindful of mother who needed her sleep. Young as we were we realized instinctively that mothers must be shielded as much as possible from the harsher facts of life.

While I got the muzzleloader down from the gun rack, a ticklish job to manage quietly, Cecil scouted around for a powder-horn and shot-bag, percussion caps and some oakum for wads. You need a lot of equipment to operate a muzzleloader.

At last we were ready and soon found ourselves stumbling round shore to the blind or "gaze" on the point. This was a hole or depression on the headland, built up breast high all round with rocks, partly to afford shelter from the wind, partly to keep a sharp lookout for birds without their seeing us.

It was still not daylight. I had left home early because I wasn't quite sure of the process of measuring the load in our "secret weapon." When we were safely stowed away we began loading. First we poured out so much powder. We had to guess at this but we wanted plenty of power so we let the deadly grains run freely. We used Cecil's hand to measure it as his was bigger than mine. Pour it into the barrel! Roll up an oakum wad and ram it down with the ramrod! Pour out a handful of shot, a good big one, Cecil's again!

The sound of the lead pellets rattling down into the barrel was music to our ears. Another wad was rammed down and we were ready for measuring. This is done by placing the hand with fingers horizontal, against the length of ramrod protruding from the gun-barrel, and observing how many fingers' width it is. Five fingers is considered a heavy load, six, extra heavy. On the top of the rod there is what is called a "wormer," about four inches of wire with a little barb on the end for getting the wad out of the barrel. A "wormer" is usually a straightened fish hook.

Cecil and I measured the load. It was five fingers up to where the wormer began. Something must be wrong. The wormer was four more, which made nine altogether. We looked at each other, puzzled. What was the catch?

Suddenly I had it. Of course.

"Sure, you don't measure the wormer," I rationalized, "That makes it O.K. Five fingers. I can stand up to that all right."

Cecil was a little dubious. He wasn't sure, as of course neither was I. This was our first experience with heavy artillery.

While we stood there, debating whether we should reload with a smaller charge, just in case, Cecil happened to glance up over the "gaze" rampart. He jumped.

"Shot of ducks coming," he whispered, his eyes popping. "About 50 I think, and it looks like they're going to be in shot. Get a cap on the nipple!"

With fingers shaking with excitement I found the cap-box, got the cover off, capsized them all, finally captured one and jammed it on the nipple.

I was on my own now. Cecil retreated a few steps behind me, nearly as excited as I was, whispering heartening but useless advice.

I raised the gun to my shoulder with an impressive flourish and levelled her over the breastwork. The ducks were streaking along in a dark-brown huddle, with here and there the white flash of an old drake among them. I moved the barrel along with them in the best duck-shooting tradition and pulled the heavy trigger. And I can still hear the explosion echoing up through the years.

The whole cliff seemed to disintegrate under the concussion from that cyclotronic muzzleloader. It flew out of my hands. I grabbed my right shoulder, trying to hold it in place, and danced about in agony. Somewhere down below the levels of conscious pain my subconscious was registering, "You've got to measure the wormer."

After a while the pain in my shoulder eased enough for me to notice what was going on around me. The smoke had cleared a bit and I saw Cecil, sitting on the rocks, with his head between his hands, groaning considerably to himself so as not to interfere with my suffering.

"What's the matter with you?" I asked with a flicker of interest, "You didn't get hurt, did you?"

He answered between groans, "When you fired, something came back and hit me on the head. Look at this bunch here."

I looked. It was as big as a pullet's egg and getting bigger all the time. Of course the good old muzzleloader was responsible.

By and by we looked out hopefully where the ducks had been. With so much havoc wrought behind the gun, surely no life could have continued to exist in front of it. Sure enough, there were two dead ducks floating slowly in toward the shore.

We picked them up and staggered home. Mother would find out about our expedition of course, but the two ducks would put her in good tune. She mustn't discover our injuries though, or there'd be trouble. I'd never get the chance to load another muzzleloader, rightly or wrongly. Cecil's cap covered his bunch during most of the day, and for a week we took a bottle of liniment to bed with us every night.

Gradually my brother's head regained its normal contour and my bruised and swollen shoulder mended. If I'd held the gun tightly I'd have broken the bone.

When father came home I asked him if I could use the muzzleloader. "I suppose so," he said, hesitatingly. "But be careful. Don't overload. Five fingers is plenty."

My right shoulder gave an approving twitch.

"I know," I answered fervently, "five fingers, and you've got to measure the wormer."

Render Unto Caesar...

The church bell pealed out, sprinkling its Sunday morning benediction over the neatly painted houses, the picket fences, the grazing sheep and the calm waters of Driscoll's Cove. Joe Lidstone put on a quicker step and caught up with Skipper Isaac Newton on his way to church. He'd know if anybody did, what Monday evening's meeting was all about.

"Well, Joe, to tell 'ee the truth I only knows what the new parson told me. He's kind of bossy in his ways, not like 'tother one we had, and I couldn't get much out of him. But it seems they got a feller goin' around holding meetings to try and raise more money for churches. Some kind of organization. This meeting is called to explain it to us. Better come along and have your say."

"Oh I'll be there Skipper. Don't know if I'll have much to say though. I'm not much of a hand at public meetings. The words don't seem to have a clear channel from me brain to me lips. Too many sunkers for 'em to ground on, I spose. There's fellers fer that though, like you and Walt Bursey." He nodded toward a grove of little fir trees, just coming to their full summer greenness. "Beautiful colour, eh Skipper? If we could only get that on our brushes when we paints our skiffs and punts. . . ."

The new parson, Reverend Bolt, conducted the service with briskness and authority. Just before the sermon he told the little congregation about the meeting to be held Monday evening. "As you know we are trying to work out a more systematic, business-like method of ensuring regular church payments. Mr. Springer, representing a well-known church fund-raising organization will be here to explain the set-up and answer all questions. I know you are all interested in the progress and well-being of your church and this deserves your support. My sermon today is entitled 'Giving to God.' I am sure you are all familiar with the parable of the Widow's Mite. . . ."

Joe didn't concentrate much on the sermon. For one thing the windows were open on this fine June morning and the minister's rhetoric was interrupted by the sharp twittering of birds and the plaintive bleat of young lambs gambolling on the new grass just outside the church. He was preoccupied too with the next week's work. He hadn't made much of a summer's wages so far and he knew he'd lose the new boat and engine he had on credit if the prospects didn't brighten up soon. After the service the men hung around outside the church gate as was the custom, smoking and exchanging news and banter. Jim Coles was praising the new parson's last Sunday sermon on the text "In my Father's House are many Mansions."

"He put it across pretty damn well if you ask me. Said we're buildin' our mansions up yonder accordin' to our actions here. That makes sense." Jim slipped in a cuss word or two as he usually did.

"Then I'm afraid you're sendin' up some No. 2 lumber there, Jim. Every time you spits out a damn, that's another knot-hole in your clapboard."

"Yes, Jim, your mansion is goin' to be leaky as a basket. While the rest of us are inside, snug as a bug in a rug, tunin' up them golden harps and singin' 'Come Home Newfoundlander,' you're goin' to be out in all kinds of weather tarrin' and puttyin'." After the laughter died down the talk got serious.

"I liked that sermon better'n the one this morning," Joe Lidstone said. "'Tis all very well to tell us to give more to God. I'd like to be sure God is gittin' what we're givin' now."

There was a general hubbub of assent. "Seems to me a lot of organizations are claimin' to be collectin' money for God," broke in another man. "'Tother parson told us God was inside of us but I don't see anybody dishin' out anything our way. P'raps this meetin' man is goin' to do something about that."

"By the way, Skipper Isaac," grinned Bill Squires, who took up the collection, "was that a gold sovereign you put in the plate last Sunday night? I han't seed one o' they about for ages."

"Yes, boy, I put that in on a mistake. Thought 'twas a quarter I was handin' over. Left me glasses at home. The parson thanked me for it and offered to give it back when I told him about the mistake. I said, 'No, I wouldn't think of it. I give it to God and t'hell wi' it'."

Joe's little boy, Tommy, went to Sunday School after dinner for the first time. When he returned the little fellow was crying. His teacher had given them all little tickets with an illustrated biblical text to learn. His was "Feed my lambs," beneath a picture of the five barley loaves and two small fishes. "She asked me if I knowed what it was," sobbed Tommy, "an' I told her it looked to me like a few pork buns and a couple tomcods. 'Tother boys laughed at me and so did the teacher. They looked just like the pork buns we haves, Sattidy night, mom!"

"Of course they did, Tommy," soothed his mother. "When you get older you'll learn the right grown-up names for things. And I bet the barley loaves didn't taste a bit better than my pork buns. That reminds me, Joe. I must pack up a little basket of food for you to take up to Skipper Will Genge when you go up to visit him after church. You're going I suppose?"

"Of course m'dear. I'm on the visitin' committee and 'tis my turn this Sunday. The poor old feller is lyin' there paralyzed from the waist down. He'll want to hear all the fishin' news. I got to finish that pair of crutches for him the first chance I gets. He thinks he might be able to get about the house a bit if he had 'em. 'Tis a job to tend hands to all the summer work. I might have time tonight after Sunday is out."

There was a fair crowd at the meeting Monday night. Rev. Bolt made a little speech of introduction. Mr. Springer outlined the plan for more and systematic giving. He had charts and graphs galore "nuff to turn your head dizzy," as Joe said afterwards.

"What we would like," he said, "is for every man to pledge a certain amount to the church, to God, for the next three years. That will be the first charge on your budget and will enable

your leaders to plan for the extension of God's work in the parish
and outside of it."

Walt Bursey was on his feet in a jiffy. "I don't understand
that budget talk very well. My income and that of every man here,
clear of the parson, the merchant, the telegraph operator and the
schoolteachers depends on whether the cod swims along by our
trap leaders or takes the bait from our trawl hooks. They baint
goin' to sign no pledge to do that for the next three summers.
I wish they would. I'd find the paper and ink."

George Grimes, the Rector's Warden tried to answer him.
"Now boys, we all knows your side of it and I reckon God does
too. The fishery is uncertain. But me and Ike Newton got to go
around every fall tryin' to get more money for the church. 'Tis
a thankless job sometimes. I say let's see if this plan won't help.
If you all signs up for a certain amount and sticks by it our job'll
be easier."

Joe Lidstone got in a few words next. "I'm not puttin' my
hand to paper for something I can't carry out. After my family
is fed I got to try and pay off me boat and engine. I don't reckon
God wants me to neglect that. If He do it's between Him and
Mr. Little, me merchant. They can work that out together if
they'm on speakin' terms."

Rev. Bolt thought that here a little dignified preaching
was in order. "My dear friends," he said, "I'm sure we are not
asking you to neglect your rightful obligations as family men.
But remember that God from whom cometh every good and per-
fect gift has first claim on you."

"We all knowed there was a God before either of you fellers
come to Driscoll's Cove." Harry Brown had the floor now. "I
can't find anywhere in the Bible where the Blesseed Lard was so
mighty concerned wi' raisin' money. If He had been He would
have left a fat bank account and precious little else."

Some of the younger unmarried men with no responsibilities
were willing to sign a pledge and said so. "I don't see what all
the fuss is about," shouted Charlie Tucker. "This plan works well
in some places. I hear the churches in St. John's went for it big.
They've more than doubled their budgets since they brought it in."

"St. John's is not Driscoll's Cove," squeaked up Phil Collins.
"Nearly every man there is under regular pay. An' there's a man

right here in this meetin' who'd better pay me for a new punt I built for him before he goes signin' away his money to God or anybody else."

"Now, now, Mr. Collins," interrupted Parson Bolt. "Let's keep personalities out of this, shall we?"

"I'm not mentionin' no names," piped Phil, "but his initials is Charlie Tucker." Phil had been waiting for that fifty dollars all spring and discretion was not his strong point.

Mr. Springer looked at the minister in sheer frustration. Rev. Bolt took another good look at his new flock. It hardly seemed worthwhile to prolong the meeting.

Skipper Ike Newton clewed it up. "I think parson, we'd better go on the way we've been goin'. I know some of us don't give enough to the church and then again a scattered one of us might be givin' too much. (Shouts of "That's you, Uncle Ike. Leave your sovereigns home or wear your glasses to church.") 'Tis pretty hard to figure sometimes if the hand held out is God's or man's. An' then again if 'tis God's we can't always tell what He wants us to put in it — pr'aps 'tis not always money. Now 'tis nearly midnight and we all got to get crackin' pretty early in the mornin'. Some of us haven't got all our day's catch split yet and tomorrow's sun don't know nothin' about this meetin'. I just want to remind you boys, we'll need a lot of help the first blowy day puttin' them new ashfelt tiles on the church floor and shorin' up the rectory. I won't ask you to sign your names to that but the church bell will tickle your ears. If Mr. Springer is here we can find a hammer for him too, can't we boys?"

The Outdoor Motor

"Pride an' flusteration," said Skipper Neddie, stuffing the obacco into his pipe bowl with a huge, spade-like thumb, "are wo things that makes fools of people." When the old salt started naking sweeping statements on human nature, I knew he was getting wound up for a good story.

"There wuz one man I knowed," resumed the Skipper, "who had the both of them faults. Proud as a legharn rooster, an' nerviser'n a she-robin over 'er eggs. Luke Bolton his name wuz, an ornery little son-of-a gun. Used to go fishin' in a punt be hisself. Had plenty of gall and wuz always tryin' to go one better chan the rest of us. If he happened to be high-liner among the hook-and-line men any year, he'd go around proud as a peacock and brag that he used his brains and we didn't.

"One spring Luke got hold of one of those outdoor motors that hooks on the starn of a punt. The old buzzard wuz always talkin' 'bout the time he wasted, rowin' out to the grounds and back agin. One of the merchants here had this ingin come for his son, but the son died just afterwards, so his father told Luke about it. Got him all worked up over the nice, easy time he'd have, sittin' down, watchin' his punt zip along. Course Luke didn't know nothin' about runnin' the thing, but he got one of the fellers around here wot's studyin' to be an ingineer at college to larn him. Adder two weeks hard work, an' tearin' the starn off his punt and puttin' a new one on, he thought he wuz ready to leave the wharf-head.

"The second day the ingin come on the room, Luke's wife, Martha, packed up an' moved over to 'er sister's, until Luke had his course finished. She told how Luke 'ud get up in his sleep, go to the gramaphone, thinkin' it wuz his outdoor motor, hitch a piece o' string on the post in the center an' try to start 'er. She used to send over a box o' Nerve Food every week. Luke never took 'em but he give 'em to the young ingineer, Joe Manning. Joe claimed that wuz the only thing that saved 'im from goin' crazy while he wuz teachin' the old man.

"I remember the first day Luke come out fishin'. I wuz out on the ground, fishin' away, when all of a sudden I hears this queer hum. I couldn't make out first if it wuz an airplane or a 'hosstinger.' I looked all around, couldn't see nothin', but the hum got louder an' louder. Then, up over a lop, I sees Luke's little crookeed-nose punt, goin' like the divil terryfied, an' Luke back on the countersate, grinnin' all over his face. He cocked up his leg as he whipped along an' shouted out that he'd give me a tow if I wuz ready to go in when he wuz.

"Everything seemed to be comin' his way fer a while. He painted a name on the bow of his punt. Called 'er the *Hummin' Bird*, and hum she sartinly did. When Luke 'ud get in, just afore dark, all the young gaffers 'ud be down on the wharves, watchin' the *Hummin' Bird* dock, and all this attention made the old feller perk up still more. It got so bad that the rest of us wuz beginnin' to think about gettin' outdoors too, an' two or three of us had sent away for a catalog, when something happened which made us change our minds.

"One evenin' I got in afore Luke, an' a crowd of us was gettin' ready to go squiddin' when we heard the *Hummin' Bird* comin'. We didn't pay much attention till she got quite handy, and then somebody shouts, 'He can't stop 'er! Something's wrong with Luke's outdoor motor!' That made us look pretty fast. Sure enough, he couldn't get 'er shot off, so he had to turn 'er out to sea agin, or she'd 'uv stove 'er stem in agin the peer.

"Well, holy ole mackerel, then the fun sturted. Four times he hove around an' made fer the wharf, an' four times he had to sheer off. Luke wuz frantic. The outdoor wuz putterin' away as if he wuz two miles out to sea instid of 'longside his own stage-head. Everybody sturted shoutin' advice, but by this time Luke wuz too far gone to take it, even if it had been any good. 'Don't the *Hummin Bird* know 'er nest when she gets to it? bawled Bert Simmonds. 'What's the matter, Luke?' somebody else shouted. 'Did ya just remember the old woman promised ya a lickin' the minit ya stepped ashore'?"

"By this time people had come from all around the cove and the fuss wuz tee-rific. An' then Luke got out his oars an' tried to stop 'er. But 'twas useless. He could only row about one horse power and the motor wuz four. We wuz all doin' our best to encourage 'im, goin' with our arms like we wuz rowin'. Aunt Sarah Coles, Luke's sister, rowed so hard, she fell over backwards, sprained 'er ankle, an' a couple o' men had to carry 'er 'ome on a handbar.

"All this time Luke's wife wuz tryin' to find Joe Manning, so he could tell Luke wot to do. Well, sir the last we saw of Luke fer a while, the oars had caught agin his chest, on account of the punt goin' so fast round an' round, an' knocked him down in the bottom of 'er outa sight. He wuz headin' straight out to sea then, an' the outdoor wuz goin' as strong as ever. He had filled 'er up with gas when he left the fishin' grounds. A full hour he had to keep cruisin' round the cove till she run outa oil, an' then he landed. The next day he sold 'er to Joe Manning fer half wot he paid."

My Political Career

About 35 years ago I was teaching in a small outport in Newfoundland when I was suddenly catapulted into politics. There was an Orange Lodge in the place and thinking that by joining I could enter more fully into the social life of the community I sent in my name to become a member. I joined.

One winter night after we had finished our business we were all racking our brains for something to enliven the proceedings. In an unguarded moment I suggested that we hold a mock parliament. At that time political interest was very keen and everybody from the Master of the Lodge to the Tyler instantly showed great enthusiasm for the idea. We had a good crowd there that night and prospects of a ready-made political career without the bug-bear of elections seized us. None of us knew the first thing about it, but being Newfoundlanders we were used to improvising. Never in the political annals of our country or of any other country, was there a government formed in such a hurry, or with more disregard for parliamentary protocol.

The Tories were in power at that time so I was elected Tory Prime Minister by everybody, including the potential opposition, and given ten minutes to form a cabinet. The Customs Officer, a man of lion courage, boldly risked his job by agreeing to be leader of the Opposition. In the fever of the moment we even forgot to enquire if he had been successful in the last elections. For all we knew or cared he might not have saved his nomination fee.

On my mettle, with the fate of the country trembling in my inexperienced hands, I hurriedly looked over my political material and made some split-second decisions.

"Uncle Bill Glover," I yelled, singling out the only man in the harbour who owned a codtrap, "you take Marine and Fisheries."

"Right you are, your honour," growled Uncle Bill, loosening his muffler and hooking a small squid-jigger bottom up in his turtle-neck sweater as a badge of office.

Henry Knight, the mailman, was a natural for Minister of Posts and Telegraphs.

Bill Searle was on the local school board so I made sure of our school grant by giving him the Education portfolio. For an amateur I was learning fast. I might want the school again the following year. After all, this political job mightn't last out the night. I noticed Bill combing his hair on the sly and putting up a hand to straighten a tie that he'd left home.

I asked the local merchant, Jim Squires, to be my Minister of Finance. Jim was pretty hard-headed about handing out favours, as he had to be to keep his business afloat in those days. At first I had been seriously considering Skipper John Parsons for the job. John was a Justice of the Peace and had some little means. But he was a bit too free for watch dog of the Treasury, I figured. He had a delightful habit of turning up at the annual Sunday School picnic with a huge bag of peppermint knobs and scattering them with lavish hand all over the "green" to be pounced on by cheering youngsters. I saw in my mind's eye John's big, generous hand dipping, not into a bag of candy but into the government chest. I shuddered and Skipper John, J.P., became my new Minister of Justice. He would, I knew, temper it with mercy.

By this time my ten minutes were just about up according to the dollar watch given to me by the school-youngsters at Christmas. I quickly completed my Cabinet and we lined up the chairs on opposite sides of the House. We had some difficulty in getting the members seated. Two members of the Opposition had already bummed a pipeful of Edgeworth tobacco each from my Minister of Finance, and my own Posts and Telegraphs was badgering him for money to buy a new leader for his dog team.

Trying to live up to his new important role in the national economy, Jim had temporarily thrown off his strict business habits. He was promising loans, squaring accounts and generally heading straight for bankruptcy when the Speaker of the House, tall, slim Peter Courtney, the tidewaiter, called the House to order. And high time too. He just saved Posts and Telegraphs from giving away his job as mailman to Opposition member Joe Bursey who had been doggedly, but unsuccessfully sending in tenders for it to the government for the past ten years.

I rescued my cabinet and we squared away for debate. The Leader of the Opposition started off with a blistering attack on my government's agricultural policy, especially taking us to task for the bad seed potatoes we had distributed the previous spring. The pent-up resentment of months was in his speech and we had to sit and take it. Imagine my horror and consternation when I heard my Minister of Agriculture and Mines joining loudly in the hear, hears of approval. Big Jake Carroll had forgotten that that was his responsibility. He was remembering only the poor potato crop and the canker in the government imported spuds that had caused it. I hurriedly scribbled a note and passed it along the line to him. He opened it and read, "Jim, shut your big mouth. In a few minutes you have to get up and answer that rat satisfactorily or your job is gone and you'll be back with an old black punt and a killick, trawling tomcods." That fixed the hear, hears from him. He got up in his turn and did a masterly job of justification for himself and us in his maiden speech, making up in vehemence what he lacked in logic. The Speaker had quite a job getting him to speak of his attacker as "my honourable opponent." Jim had some more colorful adjectives thought up and his cabinet colleagues were contributing others to him freely in loud whispers. But I was agreeably surprised by his political astuteness. He succeeded in shifting all the blame for the poor seed across the Gulf onto the Prince Edward Islanders.

"How was I to know," thundered Agriculture and Mines, "that our order for seed potatoes was going to turn out like that? I put in four barrels myself and you all know what I got out in the fall. Just enough to feed one small pig till Old Christmas Day. When I killed 'un he was so lean I had to go to the Minister of Finance there and buy good salt pork to fry 'un in. Didn't I

Jim?" This dire reversal of fortune enlisted the heart-felt sympathy of both sides of the House and Jake sat down, a martyr to Newfoundland agriculture, with his skin-booted feet fixed firmly on the first rung of the political ladder.

Foiled in their first dastardly attempt on us, the Opposition rallied their forces and attacked next our most vulnerable ministry, Fisheries. Uncle Bill Glover's face was getting redder and redder, I noticed, as he winced under the barrage of sarcasm and invective hurled against his department. His bonus scheme on vessel-building, the cull on fish, the bad drying weather — it was all blamed on poor old Uncle Bill, and my heart bled for the honest old sea-dog who was getting hotter under the collar all the time. Two of my non-cabinet men were so overcome by the eloquence of the Opposition that they tried to cross the House. We yanked them back to the Tory bench after a miniature tug-of-war with our gleeful opponents and the debate went on. I tried to catch Uncle Bill's eye to give him a heartening wink but couldn't, as he was trying to shed his big home-knit turtle-neck sweater with his pipe still in his mouth. Justice was helping him, but some hot ashes had fallen into the sweater and it was beginning to smoulder. All political differences were forgotten and the Speaker hurriedly called a recess until we could put out the fire in our Fisheries Department.

My Finance Minister took advantage of the diversion to confer with his Prime Minister, meaning me.

"Suppose they ask me to bring down the budget?" he queried nervously.

"Bring it down," I said. "It has to come down sometime. Might as well be tonight. Here, wait a minute. I'll scratch down a few figures on the back of this old school bill."

I hurriedly concocted some figures, giving Education a princely sum and earmarking it plainly for teachers' salaries.

"Better let the other ministers see this before the House resumes sittings," I continued. After all it would never do to have my own Ministers arguing about the budget after it was read and saying they'd never seen it before. I wanted to limit the argument if possible to what would come from the other side. Next I had a few words with Uncle Bill Glover and gave him a few points on answering the attack on Fisheries. Uncle Bill's sterling qualities were not what was needed in this game of mental gymnastics, and I knew his defence would not be a strong one. Suddenly, I heard my Agriculture Minister arguing hotly with Jim Squires, the merchant.

"Look here, Mr. Squires, I want another $100,000.00 to try out better breeds in sheep and cows. It's nothing out of your pocket."

Jim grinned. He was beginning to enjoy this. He had had to turn down Jake's request for $25.00 credit in his store the day before and it tickled him to hear Jake talking in the hundred thousands. He rubbed his chin reflectively.

"Well, Jake, I don't know. I might let you have $50,000.00 or so but I'll have to take it off somewhere else. Guess it'll have to come off Education. You know you didn't have that much to spend last year."

It was Jake's turn to laugh. "You should know. When I squared my account you didn't leave me much to spend."

After the House reopened, Uncle Bill handled the debate on Fisheries rather lamely and then we brought down the budget. Sniping from the Opposition couldn't have been more intense if the figures had been real.

Criticizing the Fishery estimates, one of our opponents wanted to know if there was anything in them provided for a "groaner" (bell-buoy) on Jerry's Rock just around the point of the harbour.

"That sunker is dangerous," he emphasized, "I've struck my boat's skig there more than once."

Public Works came in for a flood of requests and Jim Squires had to keep revising his figures for that department to take care of wells, bridges and wharves. He had to get the loan of another stub of pencil from Posts and Telegraphs, and the original budget made out on my used school bill had spread to cover a page torn from the Lodge minute book (the last one), the backs of four fish receipts (contributed by Finance) and an old Custom entry form (donated by the Opposition Leader).

It was 12 o'clock by the time we had all our paper used up and that was too late to start on the Dog Act, although the Minister of Agriculture who had three sheep killed by Posts and Telegraph's mail-dogs, threatened to resign unless something was done. He was mollified by the promise of a job as messenger boy for his son as soon as the post became vacant and everybody heaved a sigh of relief. We were all exhausted physically and mentally. In my closing speech I struck a serious note for education, pointing out that every Newfoundland child should have the chance to be thoroughly equipped to discuss public matters intelligently and that I was sure the night's experience had proven this to be no easy accomplishment. (Hear, hears from exhausted statesmen on all sides of the House.) We closed by singing "God Save the King" and I crossed the House to shake hands with the Leader of the Opposition.

Sea Fever

Skipper Joe Blackmore's heart was sore as he slowly and haltingly climbed his way to the "Lookout." He had known all along it was coming, but that didn't soften the blow much when it did come. His breath came harder and by the time he reached the top, he was panting heavily and was glad to sit down on the large boulder to get his wind back. He raised a large, horny hand and peered under it out to sea. Ah, there it was, the baitskiff, just rounding the head. He could see the heap of seine-linnet in the stern of the punt that was being towed behind. There was a good sea running. The sunken reef just off the cove was breaking at every cast. That was the reason they had given for not letting him go with them to haul the bait this morning. The younger fishermen had hinted broadly that he would be in the way. Caplin were scarce and the water was rough. Perhaps the next time. — But Skipper Joe knew in his heart that there would be no next time. He knew he couldn't do a man's work now. The men knew it too, but not one of them liked to tell him outright. His baitskiff days were over. He might as well face it.

It wouldn't matter so much if Harry were still alive to provide for the family and to keep up the tradition of the Blackmores. Harry had been the skipper of the seine-crew, and the best fisherman in the bay. What loads of fish he'd bring in to the stage head from the trawl grounds! He had even beaten his father's record as a lucky fisherman, and everybody on that coast knew of Skipper Joe Blackmore's catches. And yet it had been Harry to go. And he was left to fill Harry's place, an old worn-out man. What sense was there to that? How could a battered hulk like him hope to keep his end up now? He felt lost without the strength and guidance of the strong son on whom he had come to depend so much during the last few years.

The little village below him began to come to life. The men were beginning to stream out of the houses to the shore, getting motorboats ready, filling the tanks with gas, bailing out dories, taking aboard tubs of trawls, hooked out and ready to be baited as soon as the baitskiff returned with the caplin. Skipper Joe looked down on the familiar scene. In a very short time now the cove would be emptied of boats and he'd be left ashore with the women. He'd get tired of sitting still in the same place and then he'd stroll up the street. He could hear them now. "So Skipper Joe is staying in today. Well, the old man must feel bad about that. He's finding out that he's not as young as he was twenty years ago. Harry's going has just about finished him, I guess." Then perhaps he'd stop at the village store for a little spell. The storekeeper and clerks would crowd around him. "What about a yarn, Skipper? Tell us about the spring to the icefields when you carried away your blades." And he'd be foolish enough to do it. He'd get so worked up over the story that the morning would be gone when he was finished, and he'd be exhausted with the effort. Then they'd sympathize with him, and tell him that he had had his day, and quote the old saying about "Once a man, and twice a child." So they thought he was finished, did they? Well, he'd show 'em. He wasn't goin' to stay ashore yet, not while he could still row a boat and his eyes didn't give out. Jackie and Jackie's mother were depending on him now that Harry was gone. He'd have to carry on as best he could until Jackie was old enough to take his place with the men.

A young eager voice broke in on his reverie. "Hello, Grandpa! Didn't you go with the crew this morning?"

The old man turned and saw his young grandson by his side. "No, boy," he said, "I've changed my mind. You and me'll go and haul the nets today. This bit o' sea can't stop us, eh, Jackie?"

The boy chuckled with delight. Us. So he too was a man.

"Not hardly, grandpa, with this wind I think we can ju
about fetch to the nets. An' gee, I'll be able to wear that ne
suit of oilskins you bought for me."

His grandfather nodded. "Sure. But you needn't tell you
mother where we're going, Jackie. She might worry about us. Yo
know the way women are."

Jackie understood well what his grandfather meant. Eve
since his father had been drowned a month ago, the sea ha
become hateful to his mother. She never wanted him to go on
the water now, unless it was dead calm, which was seldom. Bu
he wanted to go. Besides, his grandfather needed him to hel
haul the nets.

There was that meal just after his father had been drowne
when his mother had laid the table for four instead of three
He had noticed the mistake, but he had been afraid to tell he
about it because he knew she'd cry. He had just sat there on hi
chair, not knowing what to do, with no appetite for his supper
How could a fellow eat! When his mother finally had notice
the extra plate and mug, she had got up quietly and had gon
out of the room. His heart had ached for her, but what coul
he do? Besides, his grandfather had told him that a fisherma
had to take his chance.

The two began to descend the hill to the house. Jackie'
mother had breakfast ready on the table, a smaller breakfast tha
had been the custom when the main bread-winner of the famil
was with them. The meal was a silent one. Harry Blackmore ha
been a cheerful man with a flow of high spirits, and he had love
to talk, especially at supper when the day's fishing was over. He
would tease his wife about her good looks, or compliment her on
some dish that he especially liked. Jackie and his grandfather
would listen eagerly to the day's doings on the fishing grounds.
The play of wind and tide, the relative number of large and small
cod on the trawls, the robbing of the bait by the hated dogfish,
the catches of the other crews in the bay — to all these things
the boy would listen with rapt attention. Some day he'd be out
there in his own boat. The old man's searching questions and
hunger for detail would drag on through the meal, as if he were
loath to leave the subject. But they ate now for the most part in
silence.

"There's a big sea running, isn't there?" said Mrs. Blackmore. "You'll have to stay ashore today."

Jackie looked at his grandfather.

"There's not much ground-swell," replied the old man. "Just a little wind-lop. Nothing to hurt."

Jackie ran to get the boat ready. He knew just what to do. A grapnel and coil of rope had to be put aboard. Some spare pieces of chain, fishing line, and net-buoys, in case they should be needed. A cod-jigger and line for sounding the depth of the water if they wanted to shift their nets to another berth. The sail and spread. And, holy mackerel, he nearly forgot! The bread-box and earthenware jar of drinking water. He'd be starved before they got back. He had been too excited to eat much breakfast.

Skipper Joe came down on the wharf with a compass in his hand. The fog might make while they were out.

"Got everything Jackie?" He stepped into the boat and took a searching glance around.

"Yes, I think so," said the boy. "Here's another handgaff in case the dogfish are in the nets."

The old man took his place at the tiller, while the little fellow quickly stepped the sail-mast and reeved the sheets. The skiff began to dance forward.

"Oh boy!" shouted Jackie, "This is the life."

Skipper Joe heard and the words stirred memories in his mind. Thirty years ago he had heard Jackie's father say the same thing in the same tone. Yes, it might be Harry, sitting on the thwart there, with one brown hand on the gunwale, his fair hair tossing in the wind. It was just like old times, Harry's son and he starting out to keep the family afloat in much the same way that Harry and he had started years ago. But he had been a young man then with a reputation to make among his fellows, and he had spared neither himself nor his son. Harry had served a stern apprenticeship, but he had never flinched. They had taken long chances with sea and wind. He wondered if that early training hadn't made his son a little too reckless and daring. That day of the drowning had been really too bad for a boat to venture on the water. He had advised Harry not to go, but Harry had laughed and told his father that he was getting womanish in his old age. They never saw him again. What could have happened? He had mulled it over in his brain until he was sick. The engine might have broken down, and if so the boat must have driven out to sea as the wind had veered offshore and increased in fury. Or she might have been too heavily loaded and been swamped by a breaking lop. Nobody would ever know.

"Keep 'er away grandpa!" We're just turning the point. I think she can stand a little more sheet. Just watch her rise to those waves. Like a bird!"

The Culler

Jim Parsons wiped his salty, sticky hands on his overall jacket and walked up the wharf to the business office of the North Trading Company. He was wondering why the manager, Mr. Stone had sent his office boy down for him.

"Hope he don't keep me too long," thought Jim. "Mark and the boys are waiting for them two hogsheads of salt."

Mr. Stone, a tall greying man of fifty, looked up from his desk as Jim knocked on the office door and went in.

"Oh, glad to see you Parsons. Take a chair will you. I'll be free in a moment. Like to glance over these *Evening Telegrams* while you're waiting? They just came in."

While Jim was reading the older man sized him up. What he saw pleased him.

He spoke. "Jim, I hear you're a good hand at culling fish."

"Oh, I dunno, sir. Father showed me something about it before he died a few years ago. He used to be culler on Strickland's room across the harbour. I daresay there's lots of men around here can pick 'em out as good as I can or better."

"That may be. But none of them seems to relish the job of culling for me here on this room. 'Tis not an easy job, I know. Calls for guts and decision. But there's a job for you, Parsons, if you want it, in about a week's time when the trap fish starts to come in. How about it?"

Jim took his time about answering, as he rolled a Target cigarette. Culling was not a very popular job as Mr. Stone had said. The fishermen didn't always look kindly on the man who sometimes had to throw out half their catch as No. 2, or worse still, cullage which was the lowest grade. Also he was young for the job. Generally an older, maturer man was chosen with some established position in the community. But a fellow had to start sometime to try and better himself. It would mean sure wages for two or three months and his mother wouldn't have to slave on the flake all the fall making his fish. She wasn't strong enough for that anyway now.

"All right, Mr. Stone. I'll take the job. Let me know when you want me."

"Good. You needn't say anything about this yet except to your own family. Harry Bolton is not going to like this any too well, having another culler on the same room and a young chap at that. But I can't afford to let that influence me. I've warned him for years that unless he cuts down on the drink, he'd be fired. I don't want to get rid of him unless I have to. He's been with us a long time. But there'll be work enough for two cullers this fall and I want one that I can depend on absolutely. I don't want to see a dozen skiff-loads of fish around the wharf and have to cull myself until Harry Bolton turns up after a night with the bottle."

Jim nodded. This job wasn't going to be easy. He'd not only have to try and get along with Harry, but he'd also have to convince Mary that he wasn't after her father's job.

He told Mark, his older brother about it when they were taking up the salt over the stagehead in waterbuckets. Mark wasn't impressed.

"I think you'd do just as well handlining this fall. There's going to be lots of bait now that new freezer is here. What's the big idea breaking up the crew like this?"

Jim was nettled. "What's eatin' you? Can't I make up my own mind if I take the job or not? Maybe you want it?"

"Not me, boy. I wouldn't have it as a gift. I don't relish havin' half the men in the place after my scalp. Besides, Jim you're too young. You'll have to watch that temper of yours. Chaps like Bill Pratt can be pretty ugly if they don't like the cull."

Jim swung the last bucket of salt to the stagehead as easily as if it were empty. "Bill Pratt or Jack Spratt, what's the difference?" he said. "If they try to frighten me, I'll cull the men

from the boys just the same as I'll cull the No. 1 from the West
Indee cullage."

Mark grinned. "It's not courage or strength you're lackin'.
It's tact. You'll have to cull the fish fair to both merchant and
fishermen but if the boys get riled, they'll ship their catches to
other merchants. Stone don't want that."

Jim ran into trouble the first day at his new job. He was
culling Ned Perry's fish and most of it was running No. 2 or
cullage. Old Ned didn't like it and he let Jim know in no uncertain
terms.

"Say, me young gaffer, where did you learn to cull?" Ned
had a squeaky voice and when he was worked up it jumped about
an octave.

Instead of laughing that off as Harry Bolton would have
done, Jim started backchatting him.

"Learnt by usin' my eyes same as anybody else. Where did you
learn to make this brand of dry cod?"

That was a mistake. Ned plumped another yaffel (armful)
of fish on the culling board. "You're heavin' out too many
cullage. I'm not standin' by watchin' a greenhorn crucify my
fish like this."

That word "greenhorn" stuck into Jim. He threw fish after
fish into the cullage pile, hardly bothering to look at the faces.
Ned let out a tortured yell.

"What's wrong wi' em, that's what I want to know. As pretty
a batch of fish as I ever took off my flake. What do you say, boys?"
He turned to his two burly sons down in the boat for support,
his crinkled little eyes snapping with rage. Seated on the fish
bulk in the midshiproom, they roared assent.

Jim thought, "They're tryin' to scare me because I'm new
at this game." He grabbed the man by the arm and turned a few
of the dried cod back up on the culling board.

"Look here, see this? Every one sunburnt on the backs." He
showed where they had been split with too much sun. "Now, tell
me I don't know a cullage fish when I see one." He spoke through
clenched teeth.

Ned threw the culled fish down into the motorboat. He
shook a mahogany fist in Jim's face.

"That's all you'll cull for me for a spell, me young bucko.

I'll see if I can't get a fairer deal across the harbour at Penny's. Untie the painter there, Joe, let's get out of here."

The boat's ten horsepower roared an indignant staccato, and as she picked up speed leaving the wharf, still loaded with fish, there was a flurry of talk from the other shippers.

"Old Ned didn't like the cull." "Parsons gave him some chat and he cleaned the culling board and left. Stone's not going to like that. Ned was one of his best dealers." Jim could hear most of it and his ears burned. "Next boat haul in alongside," he shouted, trying to keep the tension out of his voice.

He threw a glance up the wharf where Harry Bolton was culling. The old man was flipping fish into the different grade piles with expert wrist, at the same time keeping up a steady flow of conversation with the owner who stood at the culling board, catching the yaffels thrown to him by the men in the boat and putting them on the board back up at the speed that the culler could judge and grade them.

After the last boat had left the premises, Harry Bolton strolled over to where Jim was supervising the job of getting the fish into the big storing shed.

"You had a little argument with Ned Perry, eh?"

Jim grunted. "Durned old fool got lippy about the cull. Trying to tell me his sunburned fish should have gone merchantable."

"All the same you'll have to go easy on the talk," said the old man. "Jolly 'em along. Ned Perry owes a big bill here and if he ships all his fish to Penny's, Mr. Stone'll stand a poor chance of gettin' paid."

"I wasn't hired to give out soft talk. I was hired to cull and that's what I'm goin' to do."

Bolton shrugged his thin shoulders. When he spoke again his voice was curt.

"You've got a lot to learn. Culler has to fergit his personal feelings no matter what's said. Two things you must remember on this job. Cull 'em the way you sees 'em and don't allow yourself to get riled up. Saves wear and tear all around."

Jim walked away. There was lots he could have said. He could have hove up to Bolton some of the rumours he had heard about his favouring certain individuals on the cull. "Slip old

Harry a bottle," was regarded as good policy by some of the men. It wouldn't do any harm and paid off like life insurance. Who was to tell if a culler went easy on the fish or not? They eased their consciences by telling each other how they were being fleeced on the store goods. Jim knew the arguments by heart. He repeated them to Mary as they strolled along to the dance at the Orange Hall that evening.

"Father says there's bound to be trouble with the culling this fall unless you handle the men more careful."

"I can't help it, Mary. I don't like being pushed around. Maybe it's time there was some trouble."

"But maybe you take offence too quick, Jim. You know the fishermen have it hard enough to get along. They're bound to be touchy about how their fish is culled."

"I know and I understand that. I'm a fisherman myself. But I have to do my job the way I see it and I'm supposed to be neutral between shipper and merchant. I'm not going to be swayed by either of them even if your father is."

Mary withdrew her arm from his. "What does that mean, Jim Parsons?"

Jim kicked a stone out of the path. "Look here Mary, you know your father likes the liquor. And there's men around here willin' and eager to play on his weakness if they can, and make themselves a few dollars on the cull."

"Jim Parsons, are you saying my father lets a drink or two given in kindness make a difference to the way he does his work?"

Jim knew that edge in her voice. Mary was sensitive about her father's drinking and tried to make herself and Jim believe it wasn't as bad as it really was.

"I don't know. But the men evidently think my cull is stricter than his and I'm not changin' mine." His voice was stubborn.

"My father was cullin' fish when you were still catchin' tom-cods."

"Yes, and he's likely to be cullin' it longer than I be, if I got to copy him," Jim shouted angrily.

By this time they were at the hall door. The dancing was in full swing and the couples were tripping in and out of the sets with gay abandon. In the center of the floor on a raised platform sat the fiddler, who was really an accordion player. A group of youths and girls were seated on benches near the door. As Jim and Mary entered, one of the boys piped up good-humouredly, "Here comes the culler."

Jim flushed. It was the first social affair of any kind he had attended since his new job and he wasn't in the mood for any teasing.

"And the culler's daughter," drawled another, heavier voice. "Mary, aren't you afraid he won't grade you No. 1?"

Mary passed this sally off with a forced laugh. She was popular with all the boys and took no offence. But Jim's reaction was different. He strode over to the speaker, Bill Pratt, a tall heavily built youth with a shock of black curly hair and powerful shoulders.

"Very funny," he snapped, "go ahead, make some more jokes." Bill Pratt looked at him and lurched to his feet. "What's the matter, Jim? You lookin' for a fight?"

"I don't like that crack you just made. And I'm waiting to hear the next one. I got a good idea I won't like that either."

The rest of the group had gone tense and silent. Jim's mood was apparent and they also knew Bill's reputation for quarrelsomeness. Even the fiddler sensed something was wrong and played his tunes more softly as if trying to soothe the men's tempers.

Mary pushed in between the two. "Now boys don't let's have any fighting. We're here to dance and have fun together, not to start a row." Ignoring Jim she said to Bill, "Will you dance with me, Bill?"

Bill's face, hard and set, relaxed. "I sure will, Mary me maid. Find yourself a partner Jim and enjoy yourself. I'm shipping a skiffload of fish your way tomorrow and I want you to be able to see straight if it comes to your cullin' board."

Jim didn't enjoy the dance much. He had only one dance with Mary and they hardly exchanged a word all the way through it.

"There's been nothing but trouble since I got this cullin' job," thought Jim. I've turned away dealers from Mr. Stone and now I'm losing my girl. What thanks am I getting for trying to do a job? Might as well chuck it up."

He left the dance hall without Mary and went for a stroll around by Green Head. She seemed to be enjoying herself without him so let somebody else see her home. He lit his pipe, sat down on a big boulder and listened to the roar of the surf against the foot of the cliffs below. Yes, maybe he shouldn't have taken this job. Maybe he was too young and inexperienced like Mark said. It looked like the way things were going now Mr. Stone would fire him anyway, if he kept turning away dealers like Ned Perry. Better get out before that happened. Go to Stone and admit he couldn't handle it. But then he remembered that day in the office when the manager had asked him to take the job. "I want a man of guts and decision, somebody that I can depend on to use his own mind without running to me or anybody else to back him up." Jim picked up a pebble and tossed it over the edge of the cliff, heard it strike a few times and then plop into the sea. Under the fall moon he watched the oncoming swells, pounding, pounding against the granite headlands. Plenty of strength there. No question of giving up the struggle. Well, he'd give it one more try.

Next morning there was only one boatload of fish at the room wharf when Jim took his place at the culling board. There was no sign of Harry Bolton until around ten o'clock and he looked pretty seedy, Jim noticed, when he did turn up. There was another skiffload alongside by that time so it pulled in where Bolton's board was set up. The fishermen couldn't choose their own culler. If there were more than one man culling, whichever one happened to be free when they arrived with their fish was the culler they got. That was why when Bill Pratt's big white motorboat shot off and pulled in alongside around eleven o'clock Jim was free to grade the cargo. He rather relished the situation.

"Well, well, well," Jim greeted him, "if it isn't my friend who makes the jokes."

Bill didn't answer him. He jumped up on the wharf and strolled over where Harry Bolton was culling. Jim saw the two talking with violent gestures and guessed what it was about. Pratt wanted Harry to change places with Jim so that Bolton could be his culler. That would be too barefaced Jim knew. The other men would see this and raise a protest that could not be overlooked. They accepted the system whereby each fishowner got the culler that was free at the time, but they wouldn't stand for any switching of cullers. Bill Pratt wasn't pleased as he put the first yaffel of fish on the board before Jim.

"This is good No. 1 fish," he said. "You haven't seen any better this fall."

Jim started picking them over. Four of the ten fish or so in the first armload he threw out as No. 2. They were too salty. He said nothing. If Bill wanted trouble he'd have to start it. But he'd grade the fish the same as anybody else's. As the fish came up to him the quality got worse. Some of it was sunburnt, some dun, with brown discolouring patches caused by bad curing weather. The piles of No. 2 and cullage got bigger. Twice Bill protested, and each time Jim could feel his blood heating but he just motioned to the other to keep the armloads coming. Not yet had he learned to joke and make small talk to ease the tension between shipper and culler the way Harry Bolton did. Jim doubted if he'd ever get the knack of that.

"What's wrong with that one?" demanded Pratt.

Jim spoke quietly, "Burned up with salt. Who's your salter?"

"I am."

"You'll have to change jobs," said Jim. "Try splittin' 'em next year. The splitter you got now is no good either. Look at this round-tail. See what I mean?"

That was when Bill let out an oath and struck him, a hard blow that caught him on the shoulder and spun him around.

Jim kicked the culling board out of his way, parried Pratt's next righthander and drove a hard left to the midsection that doubled Bill over. Jim smashed a right to the jaw and felt a fierce joy thrill through him as the hard bone tore the skin from his knuckles. This was it. The end of his culling job was in sight but he'd have satisfaction in physical combat if that's what they wanted. His emotional turmoil was finding an outlet. Meanwhile work had stopped on the wharf to watch the fight. Harry Bolton tried to get between the two but Bill Pratt tossed him into the cullage pile. Nobody else interfered as the two battled it out. Jim found himself on his back wih his opponent kneeling astride him. Desperately he drew up his knees and kicked his attacker free of him. Falling backwards, Bill knocked over young Harvey Jennings who had ventured too near, yelling frenzied advice to both fighters.

Jim waited for Bill to get up. He did, and came charging with head lowered. They were near the edge of the wharf and as Jim neatly sidestepped, Bill made a big hole in the water.

Not being able to swim a stroke he came up pretty frightened and one of his buddies threw him a rope. They pulled him aboard one of the boats. Just then the store bell rang to announce dinnertime and end the fight. There wasn't much ginger left in Bill Pratt by then. He was spitting too much salt water.

Jim went home to dinner pretty thoughtful. After lunch he came back and went in to see Mr. Stone. His employer greeted him with a sly grin.

"Well Jim, I hear there's been a bit of excitement down on the wharf."

"Yes sir," Jim admitted. "I had a little trouble with Pratt. And that's what I want to see you about. I don't want to stay on."

Mr. Stone showed his disappointment. "Why Jim, don't give up now. What's your reason for leaving?"

"Well sir," Jim admitted. "I guess I've made a mess of it. I've turned some of your dealers away. And now this fight. . . ."

"My boy, if that's the way you're thinking, forget it. What I want is a culler with backbone. Things were getting too sloppy around here. Don't worry about the dealers. For every one who goes because he feels the cull is too strict, there'll be two new ones when they feel sure that everyone is going to get the same treatment, with no fear or favour shown. That's my experience.

Let's go down," said Stone. As Jim came on the wharf a deep shout went up from the men. There were ten or twelve skiffloads of fish lined up.

"Hey Mr. Stone, you'll have to raise his wages. You've got a culler that can fight too."

"Anybody that can take on Bill Pratt can cull my fish."

"The way I figger it," bawled Darius Keeting, "anything I lose on the strict cull I'll gain in free entertainment."

Even Harry Bolton was a little more sociable. "Jim," he said, "Mary wants you to call after supper."

Jim took his place behind the culling board.

"Let's go boys. First man here take his turn and haul in alongside."

The Whale

The splash of a collar buoy and the sharp stutter of a seven horse-power, mufflerless Fairbanks hit my ears as I stepped outside the shack door. That would be Skipper John Elliott, yary as ever, hi-tailing it for Jacob's ground before the Eastern Tickle crowd got the choice berths for the day. I caught a glimpse of his long, low grey-painted motorboat disappearing around the point of the island on which we had our fishing shack. Bakeapple Island it was called, a little fern and blackberry covered rock about four or five hundred yards square, one of the many in the Little Fogo Islands group frequented by fishermen in the summer.

My two other brothers, Cecil and Tom were already astir, as was father. Tom had the kettle on and the porridge pot was bubbling near the stovepipe on the little iron stove which had once done yeoman service as a drum on a Waterloo.

"Looks like a prime day for the ground," I said, rubbing my hands together. They were sore and stiff from the chafing of the hard handlines.

"Yep. Father and Cecil should soon be back from the herring net. I hope they get a score or two to help out the few squids we jigged last night off Wadham's Harbour."

Sure enough, by the time the bread was toasted and the tea brewed, the two net pickers were back with 50-odd herring and half a dozen mackerel to add to our meager stock of bait. We made short work of breakfast, jammed a couple of buns of bread, a bottle of molasses and half a dry cod in the breadbox, and boarded the motorboat moored on the collar. The other crews were getting ready too, eager to make the most of the fine clear day which would make it easy to see landmarks and to find the different spots of ground.

Ned Hinds called from a nearby skiff to father.

"Goin' to try the Pigeon today, Arch?"

Father studied the sky before answering, "Yes, 'low we will. Lots of room down that way to try about. Spose you'll be bringing up in the same berth on Wester Rock?"

Ned laughed as he spun the flywheel a few times. "Yes, if I don't be forelaid by one of them Easter Tickle pirates. We should be out there now with our grapnel down." His motor caught with a roar.

Fishing was good that day on the Pigeon Ground. Father and I loaded the punt and then hauled alongside the skiff to throw the flicking cod into the big pound amidships. When the last rounder was aboard he gave a quizzical glance at the sun.

"About half-past ten by that sky clock. Let's have a bite of lunch before we start on our second puntload. Pass back that old boiler there in the cuddy. I'll boil the kettle on the after-room while you fellows tend to your lines."

The fish were still biting although less ravenously and we yanked a few more aboard while waiting for lunch, our arms working like pistons. Between whiles I studied the horizon to the north where a score or more of motorboats and punts could be seen in the distance, spaced irregularly on different fishing spots. Most of them were too far away to tell accurately how the fishing was, but as far as we could make out none of them was shifting position or "making berths," and that was a pretty good sign that they were yanking cod aboard. To the southwest of us and about a mile away lay the Barrack Islands, low black rocks above which hundreds of white birds, starins and tickleaces (kittiwakes) could be seen circling above their nesting grounds. There were seals in there too, bobbing about in the water. About this time I figured there would be half a dozen or more upon the rocks, sunning themselves in the middle of the day. Beyond the islands and four or five miles distant stretched the blue, hummocked land of Fogo Island.

Suddenly my young brother Tom spoke.

"Whale just broke, out there a piece. A big one too."

We weren't too excited. Whales were quite common in that area. Sometimes schools of them played and gambolled for hours around the fishing boats. Soon we saw two more "blowing" in the distance.

"Must be some bait around," commented father, "herring or squid maybe. Too late in the season for caplin."

Tea was ready and we turned to at the breadbox. I had just unsealed the bottle of bakeapple jam and was spreading it on a slice of bread when we felt the boat being jerked ahead. We looked around startled. Sure enough she was moving and moving fast. I jumped to the cuddy and laid a hand on the "rode", the rope which anchored the motorboat. It was drum tight. "Hey, something's towing us."

"Must be one of those whales," shouted father. "I suppose he has a turn of the rope around his tail. Stand by to cut if it don't come clear. Here, Cecil pass the bait knife along."

We knew he was right. Only the week before Max Brinson had had a similar experience on Jacob's Ground. He was fishing alone in his punt when he suddenly felt himself being towed along and the bow of the boat dragged down by some tremendous force. Max just had time to jump forrad and cut the bar-tight rode as the water was coming level with the gunwales.

The big heavy motorboat offered a little more resistance than a punt and I didn't want to lose our grapnel and rods unless it was absolutely necessary. I delayed using the knife, watching the half hitches bite into the stem head with the strain and waited for father's signal to cut. We were gathering speed. The water was gushing away from the bow and our fishing lines were streaming out flat on the water behind.

However, luck was with us. I was about to slash the hemp when the rope suddenly slackened and the boat slowed up. The turn had come clear. We hauled in the grapnel, looked at the chafed rope, made wise comments and steamed back to our lunch grounds. But somewhere in the North Atlantic there must have been a big beast wondering what had tickled him.

Confirmation Prelude

I had come to an important milestone in my spiritual life. I was to be confirmed, at the age of 13. It was midsummer, the height of the fishing season and the Lord Bishop was making his confirmation tour around the Island. We were fishing, my father and brothers, at Fogo Islands some 15 miles away from our home, and as nobody knew exactly when the Bishop would be along, father decided the best thing for me to do was to stay at home for a week, so I'd be on the spot when the Bishop arrived. While I was waiting to have my spiritual life strengthened, father made arrangements for me to go fishing with a neighbour, Uncle John. Thus I could be earning something right up to the actual laying on of hands. On Monday morning father and my other brothers left for Fogo Islands and I shipped with Uncle John.

I had known Uncle John all my life socially, but I had never been associated with him on a business basis. Fishing in the same boat with a man you really get to know him. Uncle John was a tough old seadog with a body warped by long tussles with sea, ice and wind. He was an excellent fisherman with a natural kindly heart masked by a gruff exterior that commanded respect.

The old man fished in a motorboat driven by an ancient engine known as a "Guarantee." She was supposed to be very cheap to operate, an ideal fishing engine. She was cheap all right because she only went when it pleased her. We used to spend a lot of time sailing or drifting about and of course that way we didn't burn much oil. Getting her started was nerve-wracking for both of us. I suffered with the old man. The fly-wheel was very heavy and instead of requiring only one quick jerk it had to be hove around ten or twelve times before the engine would even consent to wheeze. By that time, of course, Uncle John would be wheezing himself. His breath would come in hard laboured gusts, the old Guarantee would gurgle, cough and for some time I'd be hard put to it to know which was going, Uncle John or the engine. If the Guarantee won, Uncle John would relax, try to regulate his breathing apparatus and scowl triumphantly. At other times the engine would refuse to budge. Uncle John would get crooked then. Baffled by some dark conspiracy of spark plugs and carburetors the old man's imagination would see the engine as something hostile, silently mocking his futile efforts to make it work. A few audible curses would escape from Uncle John's lips and back on the counter seat at the tiller, I found myself alternately praying silently that the engine would go and cursing a bit to myself in sympathy as the old man's oaths grew more picturesque.

The second day out, what I feared all the time came to pass. I was seasick. My confirmation classes with the rector had tended to strengthen my belief in prayer and I had prayed strenuously that I wouldn't be seasick while with Uncle John. I didn't want the hardy old son of Neptune to see me as the helpless, wretched, retching object I became when my semi-circular canals lost their equilibrium. But it was all to no avail. I tried to fool myself that I wasn't going to be sick. I forced myself to eat with the old man, I laughed a shrill derisive laugh when Uncle John asked me if I felt qualmish, but when my stomach finally revolted and cast its bread upon the waters, I could no longer keep up and huddled, a broken, green-faced thing in the after-standing room. My belief in the efficacy of prayer and the spiritual life ebbed fast as waves of seasickness and nausea engulfed me. Uncle John was solicitous and tried to inject some pluck into me with his heartening advice to "Get up and shake it off," but I was past all aid, human or divine. Seasickness isolates you from the universe. You are alone, you and your digestive system. You loathe yourself with a great enveloping self-loathing. Your only desire is to be left alone to die. Uncle John let me alone after a bit. He hauled up the heavy grapnel himself. And then his luck ran out. The Gua-

rantee got tired. The wind rose. Uncle John wheezed away coax-
ingly at the fly-wheel but the Guarantee refused to be lured.
Finally, Uncle John burst out "I'd sell boat, boy and engine now
to anyone who'd give me $50.00." Sick as I was I couldn't help
doing a little mental arithmetic and I came to the conclusion that
after taking the worth of the boat and engine out of the old
man's price, he wasn't allowing very much for me. But whatever
it was, it was more than my own valuation of myself at the time.

Bishops were not much in Uncle John's line. He was not a
fisher of men, he was a fisher of codfish, exclusively. He and the
cod were sworn enemies to the death and so he didn't have much
time for bishops. Not that he had anything against the ecclesiastical
order. He accepted their existence like the weather. You had to
have them. Uncle John went to church and paid the parson, but
religious forms did not touch his life very intimately. Every
evening after the fish was put away Uncle John told me to go
into the Parson's and find out where the bishop's boat was, as he
didn't want to have to leave the fishing grounds to bring me in
when the holy man came. Even a bishop was not that important in
his eyes.

Then the dogfish came. Before their arrival we had been
getting a little codfish. Now, however, nearly every time we'd
haul up our lines that pest of creation the dogfish, would be
dangling from the hook. Uncle John hated them with the bitter,
blistering hatred of your true cod-fisherman. Dogfish and engines
were two of the things that aroused him to profanity, and swear-
words, varied and colourful would curl and twist around the
engine house and strike my ears. I had nothing personal against
the dogfish. I had not, like Uncle John, spent a lifetime building
up a rich store of hatred against them. But they were making
Uncle John cuss and that was enough for me. I worked myself
into a rage far worse than the old man's. I beat the dogfish un-
mercifully against the gunwale, belaboured them with the handgaff, and cut off their noses. Uncle John's approval of all this
misspent energy went to my head and I wore myself out with
redoubled fury. But the grey, writhing tormentors still took the
bait and my language inhibitions, sharpened by confirmation
classes, gradually faded away. I started off with two or three loud
experimental "damns." They sounded fine to my appraising ears.

Writers tell me that one has to draw heavily from one's sub-conscious mind for writing material. It's the same with profanity. You start off anywhere with no preconceived pattern of cursing in mind, and your subconscious does the rest. My cuss words were now twirling around the engine house and colliding with Uncle John's just forr'ad of the midship bend. The old man reproved me. "Now, boy, if there's any cussing to be done around here I'll do it." He had a vague notion that a boy on the hand of being confirmed shouldn't be using the language that I was using. He felt a bit guilty too that I appeared to be steadily falling from grace while under his care. Then, I caught a huge dogfish and in trying to unhook it on the gunwale I drove one of the sharp bony prongs on its back into my hand. The sudden pain brought the curses quickly to my lips and from there on my subconscious took over and surpassed itself. The sulphurous stream of epithets rose to a crescendo, then slowly died away. Both Uncle John and myself stood motionless, listening, hardly crediting our ears. Then the old man spoke: "If that bishop don't soon come, my boy, he'll be too late to do you any good." From that day on Uncle John's interest in the bishop's arrival quickened. He'd go into the Parson's himself in the evening to get the latest news and he tried his best to control his language. I know the old fellow was thinking about me and I took care not to let him hear me swearing again — after all I had had my fling. I knew now what heights I was capable of reaching under pressure and was satisfied to rest on my laurels. In due time, His Lordship arrived and under Uncle John's watchful eye I knelt before the holy man. I was confirmed.

Uncle John has long since gone — not to his rest for that would be no heaven for him. I like to think that he is still fishing — in a dogfish-less world where his old Guarantee always gives him back wheeze for wheeze and no seasick youngsters are aboard to pick up any stray cuss word he throws out in sheer joy.

POEMS

Gros Morne – Bonne Bay

I am the great mountain,
I stand at the entrance of the west
Always on guard; long years have I stood
Motionless, waiting for men to gaze
Up from the level seas, waiting
While chaos swirls around my feet,
The chaos that men love.
Sometimes I call the curling mists to me,
Cool, clinging mists, that hide me from the gaze
Of dwellers in the valley,
For they must never see me weep;
I must be strong, I must make others strong —
That is my task.

Why will they not look up and gather strength?
I cannot leave my post and go to them,
For one might come along the valley's rim,
Footsore and weary with the journey's strain,
And miss my help; I must be here on watch.

True mountaineers are few.
When life buffets men,
They seek the bosoms of the lakes and streams, like a whipped hound.
I would give them strength,

Not strength of cliffs, that bare unyielding breasts
To mightier seas; not strength that trusts itself
And fails for lack of nourishing; but I would give them strength
That comes from union with the soul of things in nature;
I would teach them
How they can use the brilliance of the sun
To chase the shadows from their murky lives
And focus it on truth; to hear
Voices that rush to me
From the vast silence of the cloudless skies.
And the great winds
That keep the universe in tune with their orchestral music,
I would hire to make
Melodious harmony from their jangling noise,
And bind their spirits fast in cords of sound.

I have infinite patience.
I have waited ten thousand years
For one to leave the plains and come to me.
And when succeeding generations come
To know and seek me,
I shall be here,
Waiting.

Wanted – Wives Who Can Cook

Just before I married, mother,
I was thinking most of you.
How you used to cook a dinner,
How you made a rabbit stew.
And I used to wonder, mother,
As I gazed upon the pot,
If my appetite would suffer,
After I had tied the knot.

And I have been starved, dear mother,
Ever since I took the leap,
I have groaned with indigestion
I have lost my beauty sleep.
What a fib she uttered, mother,
When she promised to be loyal!
For the coffee has a flavour
That resembles castor oil.

I am growing thinner, mother
And I don't know what to take.
For I find my jaws are failing
When I try to gnaw the cake.
And would you believe me, mother,
Perhaps you won't but it's a fact,
When my wife puts on the kettle
She can burn the water black.

If the eggs get harder, mother
And the bacon is not fried,
I have had a hazy notion
Of committing suicide.
Though I wouldn't go to heaven,
Though I'd suffer quite a lot.
There would be one consolation,
For I'd get my meals served hot!

Tommy Decker's Soliloquy

"I'm sick of trying to behave," young Tommy Decker said,
And dug his dirty knuckles into eyes all sore and red.
"I wish they'd tell me something I could do and still behave,
But that's the way with women folk, they only stand and rave
And call you down for nothin', and then they all expects
A chap to run and kiss 'em and fall upon their necks.
My Mom won't let me throw a ball, she says I'll break the glass,
And tells me when I argue that she don't want any "sass."
She has no use for bikes and knives, she simply raises Cain,
As soon's I start to do those things that keep a feller sane!

My cousin came to visit me from over 'crost the bay,
And the way that things are lookin' now I guess he's come to stay;
All I can hear from morn till night is "Tom, behave yerself,
And take a book and read it like your darling cousin, Ralph."
He doesn't know a football from a great big "figgy duff,"
All he can talk about is books and all that sissy stuff;
But Mom she thinks the world of him and says he's worth a dozen,
And grieves and frets about me 'cause I'm not like me cousin.

I've thought about it all o' nights, and now I've formed a plan,
And if it works, I'll show my Mom that I'm a better man
Than cousin Ralph; although I 'spose he's all right in his way;
But I'd think a lot more of him if he stayed across the bay.
I'm goin' to take 'em out in punt some windy day this fall,

And "jibe" the sail right quick, just when I see a squall,
And then the boat'll soon upset and Mom, she'll yell and screech,
And then I'll save the both of 'em and tow 'em to the beach.
I dunno as I ought to try to save that sissy Ralph,
And anyway 'twould serve him right if left him to hisself
To swim or drown; but no, I won't, I'll give the boob a tow,
If Mom don't get "high-sterriks," and it don't come on to blow.
And if he drowns, I'll go to her and when she's nice and dry,
I'll tell her that to save *her* life, I had to let *him* die.
And Mom, I bet she'll come around, and then perhaps, maybe,
She'll wish and wish that cousin Ralph was a whole lot more like me."

Tommy Decker's Venture

O 'tis summer time in Newfoundland, and more'n a week ago
You couldn't see a pan of ice and not a patch o' snow,
And the trapmen, they've been takin' berths, the trawlers got to wait
Until the caplin strikes the land to get a bit o' bait.
We've been barkin' now since Monday, but we got a berth all right,
'Cos we put a fleet o' codnets on a shoal just in the bight
Where we had our trap last spring; there's a bit o' coral there
And when the tide is runnin' down, I'm feared he's goin' to tear.
But anyway there's lots o' life around the waterfront,
And after dinner, sonny, you must copperpaint the punt.
Young Tommy Decker come along, and glanced her over like,
I axed him what he thought of her, and then I winked at Mike.
I knew the boy was hankerin' for a brand new punt like that
And he's goin' to get one next year, but keep that under your hat.
What stranger, never heard o' Tom? well now, that's just too bad,
Just listen to his history, I'm fond o' that young lad.

When Tommy's father went away to cruise the Labrador,
The laddie's eyes was misty and the laddie's heart was sore
'Cos he had to stay back home; he was goin' on fourteen now
And darn it all, what could you do 'cept swim and milk the cow!
So Tommy reasoned, railing at what seemed bitter fate
And he looked as black as thunder, as I meets him at the gate.
I chats with Tom a minute, he likes a "cuffer" too.

And then he ups and tells me what's makin' of him blue.
"Can't I ship with you," begs Tom, "and help you work the trap?"
"Well now," says I, a bit slow-like, "I wouldn't care a rap
But there's me brother Jim, see Tom, he's touchy as a Turk
And for meself, I wouldn't like to cause a piece o' work."
Well, that was that; I felt for Tom, I knew what he was wishin',
I knew the boy was crazy mad to try his hand at fishin'.
But his mother didn't hold with it, she nearly had a fit
When he coaxed old Henry Davis to larn him how to split.
And every month she'd go to Tom and pay him down a dollar,
If he'd promise not to touch the punt but leave her on the collar.
She tried to keep him clear o'boats, I s'pose she thought she oughter,
But the plucky little 'angishore, he would be on the water!

Well, two weeks adder I seed the lad, I heard he'd got a crew, — —
Young Billy Dyke and Jimmie Green and that young Henry Drew.
Three smart young gaffers right enough, I know it for a fact,
Or else they'd never have the nerve to start the like o' that.
And we old codgers wish 'em luck and all the folks around
Will feel right glad if lots o' fish strikes on the handy ground.
They hauled up Tommy's old black punt and she's not very light,
They smeared her seams with Stockholm tar and made her watertight,
They took some brand-new flour sacks over to Polly Flynn's,
And paid her fifty cents apiece to make some oilskins.
(For ever since three years ago when she put his warts away,
Young Tom, he promised her he'd be a friend to her some day.)
And she's goin' to make their fish I hear, they're heavin' it together,
And Polly, she'll make it good, that's if she gets the weather.
But where they got their lines and hooks, I haven't found out yet
But I know they didn't steal 'em and I'm not afraid to bet,
'Cos Tommy Decker's honest, and just to help the lad
I give him two fine "killicks," the only two I had!

They strut about the village with their faces hard and tanned
On blowy days, and brag about the fish they've brought to land.
They "uncle" old bewhiskered salts and scorn all sage advice,
And Tommy 'lows that "Labrador" will be a better price.
I axed him 'ow he knowed it, and he started to explain
'Bout foreign markets and supply and wars in sunny Spain.
I couldn't arg with Tommy, he's smart, that boy, I'll say

And if the fish holds on a bit, he'll make the venture pay.
'Course I know he's got expenses, there's that young Billy Dyke,
He's Tommy Decker's second hand, with a first hand appetite;
He'd clean the breadbox every day, and never get his fill,
So Tommy had to go to work and 'lowance out young Bill!

There's Jimmy Green, he's sort o' quiet, but there's not a man around
Can hold his own with Jimmie when they're squiddin' on the ground.
He knows about the weather too, jest glances at the sky,
And tells you if 'tis goin' to be wet or if 'tis goin' to be dry.
And he can't be jammed at figures, he's cute that boy is, very,
So Mr. Tommy uses him as a kind of a "sekkatery"!
He made young Henry salter, and that completes his crew,
He swears they'll have no cullage, and not much No. 2.

Young Tommy says to help out folks afore they're dead and gone,
He thinks the blinkin' government should put a bounty on,
And Tommy's took up smokin' and so has all his crew,
He says 'tis everybody's job to help the revenue.
And you should hear 'em swearin', when the dogfish strikes their
[trawl,
They're bad them days, 'tis risky to speak to them at all.
Now some men save the livers, and some the oil extract,
But Tommy Decker will not stoop to such disgrace as that.
There's mournin', bitter mournin', this year in Dogfish land,
And scores of long-nosed robbers are marked with Tommy's Brand.

Now Tommy's sweetheart, Mary Rose, she's heard about the byes,
And her pride of Tommy's courage is shinin' in her eyes,
She walks from church along with him and I don't know if 'tis wrong,
But she smiles at Tommy shockin' when the sermon's going on.

Oh 'tis summer time in Newfoundland and everything's in bloom,
The grass is high enough to cut, or will be, pretty soon,
And the youngsters still go swimmin' just like they used to do,
But the four champeens is missin', they're not at the rendezvous.
And there's tomcods round the stages, thick as any boy could wish,
But Tommy Decker and his crew, they're after bigger fish!

Disillusionment

Yesterday I strolled along the beach
And skipped flat stones over the water's smooth surface.
Smiling and bland you were, my quiet sea!
I watched two fisherman's children, a boy and girl,
Sailing their toy boats near the shore,
And I heard them complaining that there was not enough wind
To fill the slack sails.
They built little castles, with the sand
And the shells you had kindly brought them;
They felt your limpid coolness on their bare feet
As they dabbled in the shallow pools.
And they praised you, and blessed your bountiful hand
Laying the table for their daily bread.

But now, this morning
From this high cliff,
I gaze on a drunken monster
Tearing the red sea-kelp from the rocks,
Striving with maniac fingers to reach
The hearts of the children.
Laughing, gloating,
Because their childish hearts do not yet understand
Your devilish villainy.

And tomorrow they will come again
And laugh into your bland, smiling face.
They will launch their little ships trustfully
As they'd seen their father launch his dory.
But in the evening when the gale breaks,
They will race home over recoiling, horror-stricken sands,
And, sitting at the rattling window, side by side,
They will see slanting men in oilskins on the beach,
Pulling the punts and dories above high-water mark,
Mooring the larger boats fore and aft.
Then they will look seaward with straining eyes
For a white motor boat and a green dory,
Riding on a wave's high crest,
Until it grows dark . . . .

"That They Might Have Life" – 1937

John knelt and took the wasted hand.
Her dying eyes caressed him; at his touch
She rallied all her force to speak to him,
Knowing he might not hear her speak again.
I listened, shading my eyes from hers,
I could not look upon a naked soul.

"Love, it will soon be ended; no more the wait
For pauper's food; no more the husbanding
Of energy that could not be replaced if used.
I am so weary of it all — — No, let me talk,
Too long I could not, but to-night
I have some strength, and while it lasts, I must.

"John, you were kind, but when I saw you, gaunt,
And watched your failing strength, the strength that once
Enslaved my girlish heart, my very soul
Clamoured to comfort you, but I could not, John,
I had no power; but like a sapless tree
That moans in agony to earth and sky and air
For nourishment and finds it not,
I prayed for strength, wordless; fearful that words
Might steal some power from me as I knelt
Besieging God.   My love, there is no God.
I tell you there is not!   Don't argue with me, John,

For if you say there is, my flickering torch
Will burn itself in one last fitful glow
To prove your words a lie.

"I could not comfort you; a deadly weariness
Robbed me of that blest role of comforter
Given to women; and then — —
I knew that once again I was to bear
A child; I had borne three.
Three manly sons; my boys, my gift to life:
But both of us had dreamed and hoped
For a girl-child; and hoping,
I summoned all my strength that this new life
Might not be cheated.

"John, do not weep; I must be dead,
I see your tears, and they arouse in me
No pain or sorrow; God, have I come to this
That I can see you weep and not weep too?
You know the rest; you know how we rejoiced
That she was born; how weak I was,
But proud that she was strong!
How worn and sick,
But glad that she had health!
And day by day and month by happy month
We watched the babe with proud, possessive eyes,
Her finely moulded limbs, her dancing eyes,
And lips that babbled to our wondering ears
Secrets — — Oh John!
I'm going mad, give me your hand,
I tell you, John, I could not give her more;
Say that I could not, won't you?
I gave her all: I robbed my poor starved body of its life
To give her birth; I drained my veins of blood
Till all my nerves cried out in tingling rage;
I gave her all I had; but not enough!

"We watched her body grow like a young fawn
In graceful movement, but her mind was blank.
What devil's trick was this? I ask you, John,
Who was it mocked our love with bastard hate?

Who gave our darling beauty such as that
And stole her birthright of intelligence?
This is your God.
No God of mine, I swear it!
My mother love,
My every claim to womanhood,
My love for you,
Cries everlasting shame upon His head!

"Ah, let me die, my love; I cannot live
And watch my baby thrive in idiocy,
Do you remember how she cried at first?
How did I know, how could I understand
Her protests at her birth's catastrophe?
You think me hard and bitter?   Perhaps I am.
I was not so at first; I tried to pray,
Tried to believe and see the hand of love
Guiding me on.

"But 'dole' is bitter bread to nourish faith.
By day a mist swam ever in my eyes,
By night a devil's voice was in my ears.
I know I'm going mad!   I'd pray to die
But there's no God to hear it.

"Kiss me, John.
It may be in the land to which I go,
Sometime, somewhere, my hungry heart shall find
My faith again, my little daughter's mind."

SONGS

A Newfoundland Come Home Song

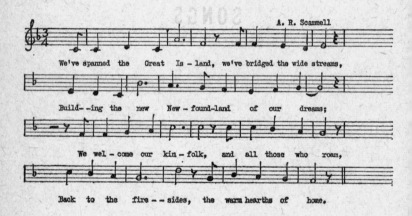

A. R. Scammell

We've spanned the Great Is-land, we've bridged the wide streams,

Build--ing the new New-found-land of our dreams;

We wel-come our kin-folk, and all those who roam,

Back to the fire--sides, the warm hearths of home.

Then come in your thousands our first Come Home Year,
Give us your blessing and join in the cheer;
Though letters and phone calls we always enjoy,
You in the flesh is what *we* want, me boy!

So bring all the family and park them on us,
Junior and Senior, we don't mind the fuss;
Leave all cares behind you wherever you are,
Start the cruise homeward, our doors are ajar.

You don't have to linger if boats are stormbound,
Don't have to wait till the steamer calls round;
There's rivers to fish in with dry or wet fly,
Guides to instruct those who Seldom-Come-By.

Discover once more in the land of your birth,
Sweet simple pleasures and sources of mirth;
There'll be lots of weddings, there's one at Renews —
Jig a few codfish and cook your own brewis!

We'll sing the old songs, there's some new ones just out,
Try out your tonsils and make a glad shout,
Nobody may ask you, so just Come-By-Chance,
Join the soiree at the Kelligrew's dance.

Our time spent together will ebb like the tide,
Distance may part us but never divide;
We want you to know we are proud that you came —
Some things have changed but the folks are the same.

The Squid-Jiggin' Ground

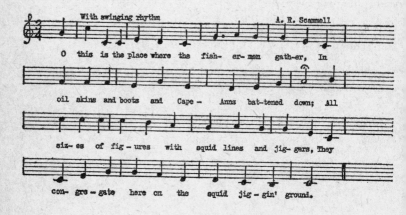

Some are workin' their jiggers while others are yarnin',
There's some standin' up and there's more lyin' down;
While all kinds of fun, jokes and tricks are begun,
As they wait for the squid on the squid-jiggin' ground.

There's men of all ages and boys in the bargain,
There's old Billy Cave and there's young Raymond Bown,
There's a red rantin' Tory out here in a dory,
A-runnin' down Squires on the squid-jiggin' ground.

There's men from the harbour; there's men from the tickle
In all kinds of motorboats, green, gray and brown;
Right yonder is Bobby and with him is Nobby,
He's chawin' hard tack on the squid-jiggin' ground.

God bless my sou'wester, there's skipper John Chaffey
He's the best hand at squid-jiggin' here, I'll be bound,
Hello! what's the row?   Why, he's jiggin' one now,
The very first squid on the squid-jiggin' ground.

The man with the whisker is old Jacob Steele,
He's gettin' well up but he's still pretty sound;
While Uncle Bob Hawkins wears six pairs of stockin's
Whenever he's out on the squid-jiggin' ground.

Holy smoke! what a scuffle, all hands are excited,
'Tis a wonder to me that there's nobody drowned,
There's a bustle, confusion, a wonderful hustle,
They're all jiggin' squids on the squid-jiggin' ground!

Says Bobby, "The squids are on top of the water,
I just got me jiggers about one fathom down;"
But a squid in the boat squirted right down his throat,
And he's swearin' like mad on the squid-jiggin' ground.

There's poor Uncle Billy, his whiskers are spattered
With spots of the squid juice that's flying around;
One poor little boy got it right in the eye,
But they don't give a darn on the squid-jiggin' ground.

Now if ever you feel inclined to go squiddin',
Leave your white shirts and collars behind in the town,
And if you get cranky, without yer silk hanky,
You'd better steer clear of the squid-jiggin' ground.

Squarin' Up

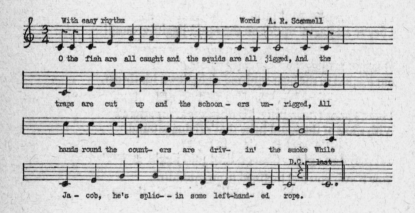

With easy rhythm — Words A. R. Scammell

O the fish are all caught and the squids are all jigged, And the
traps are cut up and the schoon—ers un—rigged, All
hands round the count—ers are driv—in' the smoke While
Ja—cob, he's splic——in some left—hand—ed rope.

'Tis squarin' up time inside the big shop,
The clerks are kept busy and right on the hop,
The men are awaiting the bookkeeper's sum,
For they all want a bottle of Hudson Bay rum.

Now Skipper John Wilkins strolled in to divine,
If his credit was good for a few slips of twine,
He got such a fright when they gave him a "ran,"
That he bought a boloney for Aunt Mary Ann.

Then Skipper John Wilkins, half-brother to John,
He asked them the side that his balance was on;
And chuckled, "Here, sonny, come tend to my needs,
A pack of those raisins without any seeds."

Skipper Harry his brother was the next to go in,
With the baccy juice dribblin' down over his chin,
And when he went home he was all in a charm,
With a box of Black Jumbo tucked under each arm.

"Say, Jimmy," said Uncle Joe Brooks to his son,
"Have you got enough left to buy that new gun?"
"I've just got enough when I've squared up my bills,
For a couple of boxes of Injun Root pills."

Uncle Dick Nichols gave his old lips a wipe,
And asked Billy Coles for a loan of his pipe,
He got some "Black Richmond" from young Tommy Hayes,
And he smoked till his whiskers went in a blue blaze.

Grandfather Pelley went stark staring mad,
He swore all the oaths that he knew, till bedad,
His son wouldn't recognise him as his pop,
Till he bought him the best pair of shoes in the shop.

'Twas all because Roberts had no "Gilletts Lye,"
Which Grandmother Pelley had asked him to buy,
The way that old codger took on was a sin,
And just at that moment, the Parson walked in.

All hands who were laughin' at Grandfather's pranks,
Were quiet as mice when they saw Parson Banks,
And Billy O'Toole, he was frightened so bad,
That he swallowed the last chew of baccy he had.

The Reverend man looked around at the crowd,
"What's the joke boys," he said, "you were talkin' quite loud
Just before I came in, who was makin' the noise?"
And he looked Uncle Pelley right square in the eyes.

"Well, Parson," said Grandfather, sheepish enough,
"I cannot deny I was cuttin' up rough,
Cause Billy O'Toole has had toothache all day,
An' begor, I was tryin' to charm it away."

Now come all you men who have squared up your bills
With not enough left to buy Injun Root pills;
If you must have enough to keep body and soul,
The only thing left is to go on the dole.

"There's five dollars comin' to you, Mr. Knee."
"I don't want it, sir, that's no good to me,
Share it up 'tween the Parson and Dr. Carew,
For I wants to keep on the good side of them two."

"If I got to niggle on six cents a day,
I'll be wantin' the doctor by the end of next May,
And maybe the Parson will have to come round,
To help me 'square up' 'fore I goes underground."

The Six Horse-Power Coaker

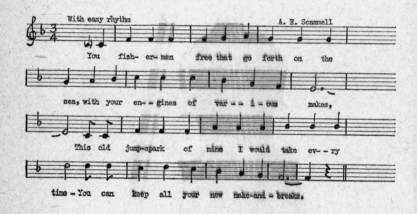

She was tied up with twine, there were bits of tarred line
Round the timer to keep it in place.
Her compression was weak and the air used to leak
Where the packing was blown from the base.

She was easy on fuel, but she kicked like a mule,
For the screws on the beddin' were slack,
And we all of us swore, when she'd rise from the floor
We all feared that she'd never come back.

So we lashed her with wire and a motor car tire,
O, how we did labour and scote,
And with posts on each side, we earnestly tried
To keep her from leavin' the boat.

This motor of ours has miraculous powers,
One summer we broke our pump band,
Now they cost quite a lot, so when she got hot,
We cooled off that Coaker by hand.

One evenin' last fall we went out to our trawl
Though it looked like 'twas going to blow.
We turned to go in, in the teeth of the wind
With a cross-handed dory in tow.

Tom hove up the wheel, and he cussed a good deal,
He cranked till he found of his heart,
He tested the oil, examined the coil,
But the divil a bit would she start.

'Twas coming on night, with the seas feather white,
When up to us rowed a small skiff,
And a bedlamer boy with a cast in his eye,
Kindly offered to give us a lift.

The kid stepped aboard, with the air of a lord,
His movements unhurried and slow;
He noted the string and the window-blind spring,
But he got that old Coaker to go.

Go, go, he made that thing go
At first he just ran her dead slow,
She hasn't much speed, cause the oil don't feed,
But he got that old Coaker to go.

Just a poor homeless lad, he hadn't a dad
And his name you may never have heard;
But the boat swung about, as he opened her out,
And she rose to the waves like a bird.

So we shipped on that kid, and we're sure glad we did,
Now 'tis seldom we ask for a tow;
And he gets a full share, which I think only fair
For getting that Coaker to go.

Go, go, he makes that thing go,
How he does it I'm sure I don't know;
We can race with the Clyde, and we'll keep her 'longside
When he coaxes that Coaker to go.

Bakeapple Jam

A. R. Scammell

Bake-ap-ple time is here a-gain we're mak-ing up a crew, My

mo-ther says that I can't go but fath-er says I can   And

when we get in on the marsh I'll on-ly eat a few Cause we
Chorus

got to stock up on Bake-app--le jam.   Bake-app-le jam! now

don't you take too much of it, I'm sav-in' it a-long till the

snow is off the ground; Just a spoon-ful or two for you and sis-ter

Sue, Cause I want to have a crock or two wh-en com-pan-y's a-round.

I picked a pint around that knap, I'll shuck 'em later on,
I'm the fastest picker here I'm pretty sure I am;
We're goin' to lose a lot of sweat afore the day is gone,
And have to pay with nipper bites for Bakeapple jam.

Uncle Isaac finds some blasty boughs and cuts a kettle stick,
Aunt Bessy brought a rounder and she shares a bit with Gran;
Then suddenly the chant is heard, insistent, eager, quick —
"Did anybody bring any Bakeapple jam?"

When garden party time rolls round to swell the church's funds,
There's food galore for one and all and little boys can cram;
On the table that's reserved for the high and mighty ones
There's sure to be a crock or two of Bakeapple jam.

Oh the parson came for prayers and he stayed with us a while,
He took us unawares 'cause he sent no telegram;
When the main course was over says my mom with a smile —
"Now have a little taste of my Bakeapple jam!"

We asked her where she kept it and we gave her little peace,
Till she turned in desperation and sternly bade us scram;
"Go on out-of-doors and play," and she'd murmur every day,
"I'll soon be right out of me Bakeapple jam."

One day a friend of dad's dropped in to share a social meal,
So we had a jar of "you know what" to coax down the Kam;
But when my mom with reverent hands removed the outer seal,
There was "fowst" on the top of her Bakeapple jam.

Whenever mother's women friends came visiting and tried
To be polite and queried her about her precious lamb;
She'd brag about my appetite with mixed regret and pride —
"I never saw his beater for Bakeapple jam."

When we cleaned the house this spring from attic to the ground
We swept out all the cobwebs in behind the baby's pram;
And under all that rubbish what do 'ee 'low we found?
But a big jar of last year's Bakeapple jam!

When I left my home that day for places far away
Said mother, "Just be careful of that parcel will you Sam?
Now don't bang this about, 'tis a few bottled trout
And my last little crock of Bakeapple jam!"

CHORUS

Bakeapple jam! now don't you take too much of it,
I'm savin' it along till the snow is off the ground;
Just a spoonful or two for you and sister Sue,
Cause I want to have a crock or two when company's around.

The Joe Batt's Arm Bully

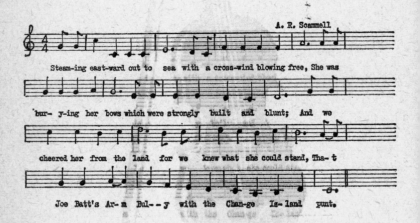

A. R. Scammell

Steam-ing east-ward out to sea with a cross-wind blowing free, She was
'bur-y-ing her bows which were strongly built and blunt; And we
cheered her from the land for we knew what she could stand, Tha-t
Joe Batt's Ar-m Bul--y with the Chan-ge Is-land punt.

Not on the handy ledges but on Carey, Crumble too
Her grapnel finds its grip, where the silvery cod abound;
See her dipping her lee-rail, cracking on with steam and sail,
That Joe Batt's Arm bully driving for the Eastern ground.

In the summer with the trawl, with the hand-lines in the fall,
Her youthful captain ranges, braving all the weather's brunt
From Round Head to the Rock, and where'er the bait-birds flock
In his Joe Batt's Arm bully and the Change Island punt.

His father built the bully, cut the spars and made the sails,
And he made them very full and very roomy in the bunt;
'Stead of building one himself he sent up to Skipper Alf
And asked if he could get him a Change Island punt.

When his dad went to his rest, he had only one request:
"Don't sell the boats and engines."   "No dad, of course I won't."
"I've taught you all I knew, you will know just what to do
With the Joe Batt's Arm bully and the Change Island punt."

Young Will he felt no fear as he overhauled his gear,
But took his father's tiller with a firm and steadfast mind;
And his blood thrilled to command as he turned her from the land,
With all the sheets strainin' and the tow-line taut behind.

She had beauty, she had grace, and she always led the chase
South of the Barrack Islands in the ceaseless summer hunt;
And sometimes late at night women wept about the plight
Of their men aboard the bully with the Change Island punt.

And one of them, a fair young maid, keeps vigil until dawn
And sees at last the far-off sails, and hears the glad "Ahoy!"
Now her heart is glad and chipper, for her sweetheart is the skipper
Of one of those stout bullies, steerin' for the harbour buoy.

As she stands there on the quay waitin' for the *Rose Marie,*
Her eager gaze sweeps outward, rests on the boat in front;
It's her own name on the prow, painted bold across the bow
Of that Joe Batt's Arm bully with the Change Island punt.

The Caplin Haul

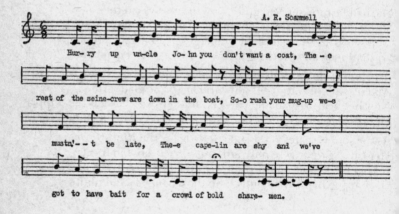

A. R. Scammell

Hur-ry up un-cle Jo-hn you don't want a coat, The-e rest of the seine-crew are down in the boat, So-o rush your mug-up we-e mustn'--t be late, The-e cape-lin are shy and we've got to have bait for a crowd of bold share-men.

Yesterday mornin', up there to the head
You could cast all you like, so said Skipper Fred,
But they've gone out since that, and they're goin' out still,
"Men, we'll want some more weight on the bunt 'un," cried Phil
    To a crowd of bold sharemen.

Alf Gatehouse's baitskiff is here on the spot,
They've shot the seine twice, but they've got no great lot;
'Tis foully bottom out here on this reef,
"What say if we tucks 'em aboard of the skeef?"
    Cries a crowd of bold sharemen.

When you'm ready you can heave away seine, Uncle Joe,
There's caplin all round us, and caplin below;
Draw in on the arms now and less of your prate,
If the seine don't get foul, we'll have enough bait
    For a crowd of bold sharemen.

Haul away on the foots there, forrad and aft,
And Cecil, keep workin' the spread and the gaff;
"Where's Skipper Tom Hinds? he's out in the punt!"
"Hold on, slack away boys, he's foul in the bunt!"
    Cries Tom to bold sharemen.

All clear, haul away, but don't close the seine,
I wish we had tied on a little more chain,
Right under the counter you can see the white foam,
"That broken-clawed killick is still comin' home!"
    Roared all the bold sharemen.

Go aisy a minute, and see what he'll do,
"He got her again," cries one of the crew;
Hurry up, close the foots, keep the heads from goin' down,
"Turn em out in the bunt, boys," bawled Uncle Joe Bown
    To a crowd of bold sharemen.

Lay hold of a dipnet, and dip away, men
If that's not enough, why we'll shoot once again;
But if that's sufficient, we'll make for the bawn,
"Look here, Skipper Phil, why this han't a-spawned!"
    Cries John, a bold shareman.

Now where he got foul, there went out I 'low
A good winter's diet for Skipper Phil's sow;
"But we've dried up enough in the seine, anyway,
To fatten the dogfish of Notre Dame Bay!"
    Roared all the bold sharemen.

Put the seine on the "gallis", one hand share the bait,
Hurry up there, my lads, for 'tis now getting late;
We're all feeling hungry, 'tis time that we ate,
For neither the tide nor the codfish will wait
    For a crowd of bold sharemen.

If you find the time dull and the hours seem long,
And you don't regret leaving your bed before dawn,
Grab your oilskins quick, there's no time for tea,
Jump into the baitskiff, come seinin' wi' me
　　And a crowd of bold sharemen.

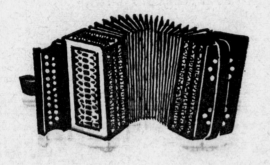

Long May Your Big Jib Draw

Words (A. R. Scammel)
Tune (Mrs. E. Anthony)

Some folks say cheer – i – o when they wave the hand to you, The-e
Eng-lish say good-bye the-e French they say a-dieu; But when Newfoundlanders
part, th-is wish leaps from the heart — Long may your big jib draw.

Chorus

It means may luck at- tend you, may a fair wind fill your sails, May your
ship keep to her course with e- ver fav'ring gales; It reminds us of our her- i-tage of sea and sail-ing men, And we'd
like all hands to try it when they say good-bye a- gain.

You may lack a captain's ticket, you may not know stem from stern,
P'raps you can't box the compass, and perhaps you'll never learn,
But try it for a spell, the way we say farewell,
Long may your big jib draw!

It's a wish from sailing days, when head winds meant delays,
And the stately old square-riggers glided graceful on their ways,
The crew would hear the shout, as the canvas bellied out,
Long may your big jib draw!

We who call the ocean mother, often wander from her side,
But she claims her children's homage, and she will not be denied;
So we pay that timeless fee, in the language of the sea,
Long may your big jib draw!

Ships may not stay in harbour, there's another voyage ahead,
Friends may not always linger, there are goodbyes to be said;
But make the parting gay, speed your friend upon his way,
With Long may your big jib draw!

Sometimes your vessel is becalmed for days and weeks on end,
Sometimes the winds of life will blow you off your course, my friend,
But the wind is sure to veer, you must stay on board and steer,
And Long may your big jib draw!

CHORUS
It means may luck attend you, may a fair wind fill your sails,
May your ship keep to her course, with ever favouring gales,
It reminds us of our heritage, of sea and sailing men,
And we'd like all hands to try it when they say good-bye again.

Glossary

Bakeapple (bog-apple) — yellow, raspberry-like fruit

Bedlamer (boy) — half-grown boy

Blasty boughs — dry, tinder-like fir boughs

Bogey — small stove

Brewis — hard biscuit soaked and boiled and served with cod

Bully — a large fishing boat with gaff sails

Caplin — a small smelt-like fish

Carey, Crumble — names of fishing grounds

Castnet — small hand net for throwing, weighted with round lead balls

Coaker — early motor-boat engine named after Sir William Coaker, a famous Newfoundland politician

Copying pans — jumping from one small cake of ice to another

Crosshackle — contradict, irritate

Cuddy — small enclosure in the bow of a boat

Fester — ulcerate (of sore or wound)

Fowst — mould

Gallis — gallows or frame for hanging nets to dry

Hosstinger — dragonfly

Killick — home-made anchor; a frame of rods enclosing an oblong stone

Leader — long straight net leading fish to trap doors

Linnet — knitted twine for nets or traps

Livyers — inhabitants

Rounder — small, dried unsplit cod

Sparbel — small shoe nail

Splits — kindling

Squires — Sir Richard Squires, Member of the House of Assembly and twice Prime Minister before the advent of the Commission of Government in 1934

Trunkhole — trapdoor in fish stage for drawing water, etc.

Waterhorse fish — salted cod that has just been washed before being dried in the sun

Yary — wary, alert